OXFORD*Playscripts*

Charles Dickens

*adapted by Steve Skidmore
and Steve Barlow*

a *T*ale *T*wo ^of Cities

Oxford University Press 1996

Oxford University Press, Great Clarendon Street,
Oxford OX2 6DP

Oxford   New York
Athens   Auckland   Bangkok   Bogota   Bombay
Buenos Aires   Calcutta   Cape Town   Dar es Salaam
Delhi   Florence   Hong Kong   Istanbul   Karachi
Kuala Lumpar   Madras   Madrid   Melbourne
Mexico City   Nairobi   Paris   Singapore
Taipei   Tokyo   Toronto

and associated companies in
Berlin   Ibadan

Oxford is a trade mark of Oxford University Press

A Tale of Two Cities adaptation and activities
© Steve Barlow and Steve Skidmore 1996
First printed by Oxford University Press 1996

ISBN 0 19 831292 X

Typeset by AFS Image Setters Ltd, Glasgow

Printed and bound by Cambridge University Press

The illustrations are by John Holder.

Diagram on p 159 is by Stefan Chabluk.

The illustrations on pp 140 and 141 are taken from
The Oxford Illustrated Dickens: A Tale of Two Cities by
Charles Dickens, published by Oxford University Press,
1949.

The publishers would like to thank the following for
permission to reproduce photographs:

Camera Press p 148 (left); The Mansell Collection p 143
and p 145; Rex Features p 148 (right), p 149 (both).

Contents

Characters
. . . .

*In order of their
appearance on stage*

Citizen 1	*Eight citizens of Paris form the chorus*
Citizen 2	
Citizen 3	
Citizen 4	
Citizen 5	
Citizen 6	
Citizen 7	
Citizen 8	
Coachman	*Driver of the Dover mail; also called Tom*
Mr Jarvis Lorry	*Clerk at Tellson's Bank, London*
Guard	*Guard of the Dover mail; also called Joe*
Miss Lucie Manette	*French born daughter of Doctor Manette; a ward of Tellson's Bank during Manette's imprisonment*
Miss Pross	*Englishwoman; Lucie's companion*
Mr Jerry Cruncher	*Messenger for Tellson's Bank, London*
Gaspard	*Citizen of the Saint-Antoine district of Paris*
Monsieur Ernest Defarge	*Wine seller from the Saint-Antoine district of Paris; a central character in the Revolution*
Madame Thérèse Defarge	*Wife of Ernest Defarge; a central character in the Revolution*
Jacques 2	*Citizens of Saint-Antoine with Republican sympathies*
Jacques 3	
Jacques 4	
Doctor Alexandre Manette	*French physician, imprisoned without trial in the Bastille, Paris for eighteen years; father of Lucie*
Mr Stryver	*English barrister; colleague of Sydney Carton; leads the defence of Charles Darnay at the Old Bailey*

Mr Sydney Carton	*English barrister who bears a strong resemblance to Charles Darnay*
Spectator	*At the trial of Charles Darnay, the Old Bailey*
Clerk of the Court	*At the trial of Charles Darnay, the Old Bailey*
Official Voice	*At the trial of Charles Darnay, the Old Bailey*
Judge	*Presiding over the trial of Charles Darnay at the Old Bailey*
Mr Charles Darnay	*French aristocrat who renounces his title to live in England and work as a teacher*
Two Jailers	*Darnay's escort (non-speaking)*
Mr John Barsad	*Englishman; a spy and an informer*
The Marquis	*French aristocrat (Darnay's uncle) about sixty years old; now out of favour at court, he has retreated to his château*
Driver	*Of the Marquis' carriage (non-speaking)*
Chief Lackey **Lackey 1** **Lackey 2** **Lackey 3**	*Four lackeys (non-speaking) who wait upon the Marquis*
Roadmender	*Working near the Marquis' château*
Gabelle	*Servant of the Marquis*
The Vengeance	*Woman friend and worshipper of Madame Defarge, known for her dedication to the Revolution*
Customer 1 **Customer 2**	*Customers at the Defarges' wine shop*
Clergyman	*Marries Lucie and Darnay*
Jailer	*Captured by the mob at the storming of the Bastille*
Officer	*In charge at the barrier to the city of Paris on Darnay's return to France*
Jailer	*In charge of Darnay on his imprisonment in Paris*

Gentleman	*Prisoner in La Force*
Aristocrat 1 ⎫	
Aristocrat 2 ⎪	
Aristocrat 3 ⎪	
Aristocrat 4 ⎬	*Prisoners in La Force (non-speaking)*
Aristocrat 5 ⎪	
Aristocrat 6 ⎪	
Aristocrat 7 ⎭	
President	*Of the Tribunal*
The Marquis' Brother	*Powerful French aristocrat (Darnay's father)*
Woman	*Young peasant woman abused by the Marquis and his brother*
Boy	*Young peasant boy injured by the Marquis' brother for trying to avenge the treatment of his family*
Girl	*Young seamstress condemned to die by the guillotine*

The following scenes require extra non-speaking parts.

Prologue, Scene 1	*Passengers on the Dover mail*
Prologue, Scene 2	*Citizens of Saint-Antoine*
Act 1, Scene 1	*Spectators and jury at the Old Bailey*
Act 1, Scene 2	*Crowd on the streets of Paris*
	Group of peasants by the Marquis' château
Act 1, Scene 5	*Mob at the storming of the Bastille*
	Defenders of the prison, fighting the mob
Act 2, Scene 3	*Spectators at the first Tribunal*
Act 2, Scene 5	*Spectators at the second Tribunal*
Act 2, Scene 9	*Aristocrats and spectators at the foot of the guillotine*

A Note on the Set

The set consists of wooden crates, barrels, furniture, boxes, wicker baskets etc. piled higgledy-piggledy. Wherever possible, furniture and set elements used in the action should be dragged off the pile, and replaced after use.

This pile of lumber must leave enough space on the stage for a small, relatively enclosed area upstage centre (an 'inner' stage) which is raised above the stage floor. Below this is a large acting area centre stage and downstage centre, and smaller acting areas downstage left and downstage right .

Thus, when Lucie first sees her father in his cell (Prologue, Scene 2), this is played in the upstage centre raised area. The two areas: downstage left and right can be used when the action divides (for example, the storming of the Bastille and the wedding [Act 1, Scene 5], or during Doctor Manette's story told during the second Tribunal [Act 2, Scene 5]). The main action should take place on the main centre stage area. The lumber pile can represent the Old Bailey, the walls of the Bastille, or (with the addition of a ragged tricolour) a barricade in Revolutionary Paris.

The guillotine could be represented by a shadow-play model. (See the note in the Activities section, p 159.)

An asterix (*) in the text indicates that ideas for staging that particular part of the playscript may be found in the Activities section on pages 158-159. The use of quotation marks in stage directions, for example, Defarge 'opens the shutters', indicates that the action is mimed and the object is imaginary.

Prologue
· · · · · · · · · · ·

Scene 1

England: the Dover Road, just outside London. Barrels, boxes and hampers are placed downstage to represent a mail coach. It is the early hours of the morning and as the lights come up, they reveal **Lucie Manette, Mr Jarvis Lorry, Miss Pross** *and several coach passengers, muffled against the cold and half-asleep. The* **coachman** *(Tom) and the* **guard** *(Joe) are sitting at each end of the coach. They are surrounded by the eight* **Citizens.**

Citizen 1   It was the best of times.

Citizen 2   It was the worst of times.

Citizen 3   It was the age of wisdom.

Citizen 4   It was the age of foolishness.

Citizen 5   It was the season of light.

Citizen 6   It was the season of darkness.

Citizen 7   It was the spring of hope.

Citizen 8   It was the winter of despair.

Citizen 1   On the throne of England sat . . .

Citizen 2   . . . a king with a large jaw . . .

Citizen 3   . . . and a queen with a plain face.

Citizen 4   On the throne of France sat . . .

Citizen 5   . . . a king with a large jaw . . .

Citizen 6   . . . and a queen with a fair face.

Citizen 7	And to all the great lords of these great nations, it was as clear as crystal...
Citizen 8	...that things in general were settled for ever.
All Citizens	(*Together*) It was the year of Our Lord seventeen hundred and seventy-five.

*We hear the rattle of the coach and the beat of hooves. The **Citizens** scatter and exit as the coach passengers come to life. The **coachman** and the **guard** are nervously on the lookout for highwaymen.*

Coachman	Whrooooah!

*The **coachman** hauls on the reins and the coach comes to a halt. **Lorry** gets down, and shouts up.*

Lorry	Trouble, coachman?
Coachman	Shooter's Hill, sir.

The other passengers groan and begin to get down.

Lorry	I hear this road is much frequented by highwaymen.
Guard	Got to skid the wheels, sir.
Lorry	Is that necessary?
Guard	That depends, sir, on whether you want us to reach the bottom in one piece, or several.

Hoofbeats can be heard, in the distance but approaching.

Coachman	Ssssh! Joe!
Guard	What do you say, Tom?

Coachman	I say a horse at a canter coming up, Joe.
Guard	I say a horse at a gallop, Tom.

> *The **coachman** and the **guard** seize guns, which they point off in the direction of the approaching hooves. The hooves clatter to a halt.*

Guard	Yo there! Stand! I shall fire!
Cruncher	(*Off stage*) Is that the Dover mail?
Guard	Never you mind what it is! What are you?
Cruncher	(*Off stage*) I want a passenger, if it is. A Mr Jarvis Lorry.

> *Lorry gives a start. The other passengers (except Lucie and Miss Pross) draw away from him. The **coachman** and **guard** eye him with suspicion.*

Guard	(*Calling off*) Keep where you are.
Lorry	Who wants me? Is it Jerry?
Coachman	(*To guard*) I don't like Jerry's voice, if it is Jerry.
Guard	Aye, he's hoarser than suits me, is Jerry.
Cruncher	(*Off stage*) I've a message, Mr Lorry, from T and Co.
Lorry	Let him come close, coachman. He's a messenger from my bank.
Coachman	(*Calling off*) Come on a footpace. And if you've pistols about you, keep your hands off 'em.

> *Jerry Cruncher enters. He moves cautiously but hands **Lorry** his message and stands his ground.*

Lorry	Coachman, I belong to Tellson's Bank. I am going to our Paris branch on business. Here's a crown for you. May I read this?
Coachman	If so be as you're quick, sir.

*Lorry reads as **Lucie** and **Miss Pross** watch him in apprehension. **Lucie** approaches and takes his arm.*

Lucie	Mr Lorry? What is the matter? Is it bad news?
Miss Pross	Now, my lamb; now, my pretty...
Lorry	Bad news? Ah...no.

*He passes the letter to **Lucie** and stands to one side, lost in thought.*
*A spotlight isolates **Lucie** as she reads the letter. The **Citizens** enter and read it aloud over her shoulder.*

Citizen 1	The letter speaks of a customer of the bank, one Monsieur Manette...
Citizen 2	...a doctor of the town of Beauvais, who married an English lady...
Citizen 3 and 4	(*Ironically*)...ooooohhhhh!...
Citizen 1	...and then...
Citizen 5	...unfortunately...
Citizen 1	...died.
Citizen 6	At least, so his daughter Lucie has always been told.
Citizen 1	His daughter?

Citizen 5 indicates Lucie and signs 'sh'.

Citizen 1	Ah!

Citizen 6	But this letter says, he did not die...
Citizens 7 and 8	Did not die?
Citizen 6	...but suddenly, and silently disappeared.
Citizen 3	And though his wife implored the King of France...
Citizen 4	...the Queen...
Citizen 5	...the court...
Citizen 7	...the clergy...
Citizen 3	...for any tidings of him, all was in vain.
Citizen 2	So when she bore her absent husband a little child...
Citizen 4	(*Indicating Lucie*)...a little girl...
Citizen 1	Ah!
Citizen 2	...she determined to spare her poor daughter the agony she suffered...
Citizen 7	...by letting her believe that her father was dead.
Citizen 1	And two years later...
Citizen 2	...the mother died.
Citizen 3	And the father...
Citizen 4	...the doctor...
Citizen 3	...the father wore his heart out in prison, through the lingering years.
Citizen 4	But now...

The lights begin to brighten. It is dawn.

All Citizens	...now...

Citizen 4	. . . now, he has been found!
Citizen 6	He is alive!
Citizen 8	Greatly changed . . .
Citizen 6	. . . but alive!
Citizen 8	Almost a wreck.
Citizen 6	Still, alive!
All Citizens	Alive!

Lucie holds the letter out to Lorry.

Lucie	Alive? My father? Alive?
Miss Pross	My ladybird! (*She hugs Lucie wildly*)
Lorry	(*To the world at large*) Eighteen years. Gracious Creator of Day! To be buried alive for eighteen years!

*The **coachman** and the **guard** prepare to depart.*

Coachman	Allll aboard!

*The passengers scramble into the coach, **Lorry** aiding the thunderstruck **Lucie**.*

Cruncher	Mr Lorry! Sir! Is there an answer?

The sound of reins and the clatter of hooves signal that the coach has started to move.

Lorry	(*Leaning from the coach*) An answer, Jerry? My answer is, 'Recalled to Life!'.

*The **Citizens** wave as the coach departs. **Cruncher** glides backwards* to give the impression that the coach is in motion, and exits.*

Coachman   (*To guard*) Joe! Did you hear the message?

Guard   I did, Tom.

Coachman   What did you make of it, Joe?

Guard   Nothing at all, Tom.

Coachman   That's a coincidence then. I made the same of it myself.

The lights fade to black.

. . . .

Scene 2

The rattle of the coach is followed by a terrific crash. A voice from the darkness shouts 'Wine!'. Many voices take up the cry.
When the lights go up, a sign stage left indicates that we are outside the Defarges' wine shop in Saint-Antoine, a poor district of Paris. The pieces of the coach have been scattered. A large broken barrel lies on its side. All the **Citizens** *(and others) race in and crowd around.*
Gaspard enters, laughing. The following speech is divided between members of the crowd.

Crowd   Wine, wine! ... See, it is wine! ... A barrel has burst ... They were taking it to market ... The axle snapped ... it tumbled from the cart ... the hoops burst ... it's lying between the cobbles ... little pools ... bring cups ... bring spoons ... use your handkerchief ... use your hands ...'

Others enter and join the crowd in scooping up the wine up as suggested above, or lapping it up like animals. Eventually, Gaspard stands.

Gaspard	See, my friends! The wine mixes with the mud.

He holds up a hand that drips red.

Citizen 5	The place where this wine has fallen...
Citizen 6	...where the poor lick at it like dogs...
Citizen 7	...mixed with the mud of the gutter...
Citizen 8	...is our suburb of Paris...
All Citizens	...Saint-Antoine.
Citizen 1	Saint-Antoine! (*Spits*)
Citizen 2	Here, the young look old, and every face bears the sign of...
Citizens 3 and 4	...hunger!
Citizen 5	In the wretched clothing hanging on poles and lines...
Citizens 7 and 8	...hunger!
Citizen 6	Staring down from the smokeless chimneys...
Citizen 2	...staring up from the filthy street...
Citizens 3, 4, 7, and 8	...hunger!
Citizen 5	In every dead-dog sausage...
Citizen 6	...in every small loaf of bad bread...
All Citizens	...hunger!
Citizen 1	Can this wine relieve our hunger?
All Citizens	No!
Citizen 5	Can this wine slake our thirst?

All Citizens	No!
Citizen 7	What can end our hunger? Citizens, what?
Gaspard	This!

> *The wineseller **Ernest Defarge** and **Mme Thérèse Defarge** enter and watch as **Gaspard** runs his dripping hand over a surface on the barricade, and scrawls in red the word, 'blood'. The crowd falls silent.*

Defarge	Say, then, my Gaspard, what do you do there?
Gaspard	(*Sulkily*) It is not your wine, Defarge. The people from the market did it.
Defarge	(*Smearing the slogan*) What now? Are you insane? Why do you write in the public streets?

> *Members of the crowd mutter rebelliously.*

Gaspard	It is not your wine! It is not your affair!

> *There is a sudden silence as **Lorry** and **Lucie** enter. The **Citizens** follow their progress with suspicion. Nervously, **Lorry** approaches the stony-faced **Defarge** and whispers in his ear. **Defarge** starts, becomes attentive, looks long and hard at Lucie, and nods.*

Defarge	Go home, citizens; the wine is gone. For those who require more, if you will enter the shop, my wife will oblige you.

> *Grumbling, the crowd breaks up; some wander off, others approach **Mme Defarge**, who gives her husband a hard look, then leads them off stage into the wine shop.*
> *
Defarge looks towards Lucie and Lorry, then looks upwards. He is evidently staring at something far aloft.*

Defarge   It is very high; it is a little difficult. Better to begin slowly.

The lights dim until only the downstage area is lit. The upstage raised area is set as the Defarges' attic room. **Doctor Manette** *enters upstage in darkness.*
Defarge leading, then **Lorry**, *then* **Lucie**, *begin to ascend a long stair*, from stage right to stage left downstage.* **Jacques 2, 3 and 4** *enter downstage right and peer at the unlit upstage raised area through a 'keyhole'.*

Lorry   (*To Defarge*) Is he alone?

Defarge   Alone! God help him, who should be with him?

Lorry   Is he always alone then? (*Defarge turns and nods*) Of his own desire?

Defarge   Of his own necessity. He is as he was when I first saw him.

Lorry   He is greatly changed?

Defarge   Changed!

Defarge gives a cry of animal rage. **Lorry** *starts back and is steadied by* **Lucie**. *Defarge calms and takes out a large key, turns, and continues to ascend stage left to stage right, downstage.*

Lorry   The door is locked then, my friend?

Defarge   Ah. Yes.

Lorry   You think it necessary to keep the unfortunate gentleman so retired?

Defarge   I think it necessary to turn the key.

Lorry   Why?

Defarge	Why? Because he has lived so long, locked up, that he would be frightened – rave – tear himself to pieces – die – if his door was left open.
Lorry	Is it possible?
Defarge	Is it possible? Yes. A beautiful world we live in. Long live the Devil. Let us go on.

> *Lucie, bewildered, catches at **Lorry's** arm. As Defarge's party approaches, **Jacques 2, 3** and **4** turn to Defarge.*

Lorry	Courage, dear Miss Manette. The worst will be over in a moment. It is merely a matter of business...

> *Lorry breaks off as he catches sight of the three Jacques.*

Jacques 2	(*To Defarge*) Is all well, Jacques?
Defarge	All is well, Jacques.

> *Jacques 2 nods and leads his companions silently past Defarge and his party (descending the stairs) and off stage. There is a silence.*

Lorry	(*Quivering with indignation*) Do you make a show of Monsieur Manette?
Defarge	I show him, in the way you have seen, to a chosen few.
Lorry	Is that well?
Defarge	I think it is well. I show him to men of my name – Jacques is my name – to whom the sight is likely to do good.
Lorry	(*Tightly*) I do not understand.
Defarge	You are English. One moment.

Defarge turns the key in the 'lock'. Simultaneously, the upstage raised area is illuminated to reveal a dark and cluttered apartment where a white-haired man sits at a bench making shoes.

Lorry   A matter of business, dear miss. Merely business.

Lucie   (*Hanging back*) I am afraid of it.

Lorry   Of it? What?

Lucie   I mean of him. Of my father.

Lorry leads her into the room. Defarge approaches the bench.

Defarge   Good day!

Manette   (*Faintly*) Good day.

Defarge   You are still hard at work then?

Manette   Yes... I am working.

Defarge   I want to let in a little more light here. You can bear a little more?

Manette   I must bear it, if you let it in.

Defarge 'opens the shutters'. A bright beam of light ★ strikes Doctor Manette, who shields his eyes. Defarge beckons Lorry.

Defarge   Are you going to finish that pair of shoes today?

Manette   I suppose so. I don't know.

Lorry is now standing beside Manette. Manette looks up at him, showing no surprise or recognition, then away again, becoming once more absorbed in his shoes.

Defarge	You have a visitor, you see.
Manette	What did you say?
Defarge	Here is a visitor. Come! Show him that shoe you are working on.

Manette hesitantly holds out the shoe.

Defarge	Take it, monsieur.

Lorry takes the shoe.

Defarge	Tell monsieur what kind of shoe it is, and the maker's name.

There is a long pause.

Manette	I forget what it was you asked me.
Defarge	I said, couldn't you describe the kind of shoe, for monsieur's information?
Manette	It is a young lady's walking shoe. It is in the present mode.
Defarge	And the maker's name?

*There is another long pause. **Manette** fidgets.*

Manette	Did you ask me for my name?
Defarge	Yes.
Manette	One Hundred and Five, North Tower.
Defarge	Is that all?
Manette	One Hundred and Five, North Tower.

*With a weary sound, **Manette** returns to his work.*

Lorry	You are not a shoemaker by trade?

Manette	I asked leave to teach myself, and I got it with much difficulty, after a long while, and I have made shoes ever since.
Lorry	Monsieur Manette, do you remember nothing of me? (*He indicates Defarge*) Do you remember nothing of this man? Your old servant? Of myself, your old banker? Is there no old time rising in your mind, monsieur?

> *Manette seems for a moment to remember something, but then sighs, and is about to turn back to his work when **Lucie** comes forward, and kneels before him. Tears stream down her face. Taking his hand, she strokes it.*

Manette	What is this? Who are you?

> *Lucie shakes her head. She cannot speak. **Manette** reaches down and touches her hair.*

Manette	(*In wonder*) It is the same. How can it be?

> *Lucie embraces him. Hesitantly, **Manette** returns the embrace.*

Manette	She laid her head on my shoulder, that night when I was summoned out – she had a fear of my going, though I had none.

> *Manette runs a few strands of Lucie's hair through his fingers.*

Manette	And when I was brought to the North Tower, they found these upon my sleeve... How was this? Was it you ?

> *Manette grips **Lucie** so fiercely that **Defarge** and **Lorry** step forward.*

Lucie	(*Without turning*) I entreat you, good gentlemen, do not come near us, do not speak, do not move!

Manette   Whose voice was that? (*He gazes on her face*) No, no, no . . . you are too young, it cannot be. She was . . . and he was . . . I was . . . before the slow years of the North Tower – ages ago.

Lucie   Oh, sir, at another time you shall know my name, and who my mother was, and who my father. If you hear in my voice any resemblance to a voice that once was sweet music in your ears, weep for it, weep for it. And when I tell you my name, and of my father who is living, and my mother who is dead, weep for it! Weep for her, then, and for me!

> *Lucie* buries her face in *Manette's* lap.
> *Manette* strokes her hair with tenderness
> and wonder. *Mme Defarge* appears and
> watches the scene with a face of stone.

Lorry   (*Whispers*) Recalled to life!

> *The lights slowly fade.*

. . . .

Act 1
· · · · · · ·

Scene 1

*The lights come up to reveal the court of
the Old Bailey. Spectators crowd the
public benches, jurors look self-important.
Jarvis Lorry sits with **Mr Stryver** and
Sidney Carton, the defence lawyers, who
whisper urgently and consult their
documents.
The eight **Citizens**, wearing lawyers' wigs,
become the prosecuting counsel.
The **Clerk of the Court** takes up a
position below the Judge's bench.
Jerry Cruncher enters and squeezes his
way onto the public benches.*

Cruncher   What's on?

Spectator   Nothing yet.

***Cruncher** shows his annoyance at such
literal-mindedness.*

Cruncher   What's coming on?

Spectator   The treason case.

Cruncher   The quartering one, eh?

*Throughout the following speech,
Cruncher tries to attract Lorry's
attention.*

Spectator   Ah! You seen them do that? What they do is, they half hang
him, then slit him open and take his insides out an' burn 'em
while he looks on (that's a good bit) and then they chop his
head off and cut him in quarters. That's the sentence.

Cruncher   If he's found guilty, you mean to say.

Spectator   Oh, they'll find him guilty, don't you be afraid of that.

Lorry finally notices Cruncher and nods to him.

Spectator   What's *he* got to do with the case?

Cruncher   Blest if I know.

Spectator   What have *you* got to do with it, then?

Cruncher   Blest if I know that, either.

*The **spectator** sulks. The court stirs.*

Official Voice   (*Off stage*) Be upstanding! . . . Silence in court! . . . Court is now in session! . . . Make way for his lordship!

*The **Judge** enters and makes a great show of bowing to the defence and prosecution. Simultaneously, **Charles Darnay** enters escorted by two **jailers**. There is much excitement. The **Judge** sits.*

Judge   (*Banging his gavel*) Silence in court.

The noise dies down.

Judge   The Clerk of the Court will read the charge against the prisoner Darnay.

*The **Clerk of the Court** stands.*

Clerk   (*Nervously*) Charles Darnay . . . yesterday you did plead not guilty to an in . . . in . . . indictment, denouncing you as a false traitor to our serene, illustrious, excellent . . .

Judge   Get on with it, man!

Clerk   . . . er . . . and so forth, prince, our Lord King George, by reason of your having assisted Lewis . . .

Judge   *Lewis ?*

*The spectators mutter. The **Clerk of the Court** shows the **Judge** the charge sheet and whispers to him.*

Clerk The French king, m'lud.

Judge (*Exasperated*) Louis !

Clerk Lewis . . . in his wars against our said serene, illustrious, excellent . . .

Judge Yes, yes, we know all that!

Clerk . . . princeourlordkinggeorge, by wickedly, falsely, and traitorously revealing to the said French Lewis . . .

Judge (*Furious*) Louis !

Clerk (*Flustered*) . . . secret military information concerning the armies of our said illustrious, excellent . . .

*The **Judge** coughs threateningly.*

Clerk . . . and so forth, er . . . so help you God.

*The **Clerk of the Court** sits in confusion. There is a stir at the back of the court. The **Judge** glares. **John Barsad**, **Lucie** and **Doctor Manette** enter. **Cruncher** nudges the spectator.*

Cruncher I've seen that grisly-looking fellow before.

Spectator Oh, he's often here.

Cruncher Ah. One o'those informers, is he? What about the old man and the girl? Who are they?

Spectator Couple of Frenchies come to live in London. That's old Doctor Manette, him what was kept prisoner in the Bastille. He's a witness.

Cruncher	And the girl? I've seen her before, must be a good few years ago.
Spectator	His daughter. She's a witness too.
Cruncher	For which side?
Spectator	Against.
Cruncher	Against which side?
Spectator	The prisoner's.
Judge	I call upon the prosecution to begin its case.

> *Cruncher sits back as the Citizens rise to speak. They launch into the prosecution case with exaggerated gestures.*

Citizen 1	M'lud, I have to inform the jury that the prisoner before them ...
Citizen 2	...though young in years...
Citizen 1	...is old in treasonable practices which claim the forfeit of his life.
Citizen 7	Indeed, gentlemen of the jury, you will never be able to lay your heads upon your pillows...
Citizen 6	...nor endure the notion of your children laying their heads upon their pillows...
Citizen 7	...in short, there can never be any question of any heads being laid on any pillows whatsoever...
Citizen 1	...until you have found the prisoner guilty and seen his head taken off.
Citizen 3	For many years, the prisoner has been in the habit of passing...
Citizen 4	...and repassing...

Citizen 3   ...between France and England on secret business, of which he can give no honest account.

Citizen 5   This treachery might have gone unnoticed indefinitely, had not Providence put it into the heart of a person beyond fear...

Citizen 6   ...beyond reproach...

Citizen 5   ...to ferret out the prisoner's foul schemes, and...

Citizen 7   ...stricken with horror...

Citizen 5   ...to disclose them to His Majesty's Privy Council.

Citizen 8   You shall hear how this person, a man of...

Citizen 1   ...sublime honesty...

Citizen 2   ...irreproachable virtue...

Citizen 3   ...and unimpeachable integrity...

Citizen 8   ...patriotically rifled through the prisoner's belongings, and stole his papers.

Citizen 8 holds aloft the papers. There is spontaneous applause from the spectators.

Clerk   Call the first witness: John Barsad.

John Barsad takes the stand.

Citizen 4   Your name is John Barsad?

Barsad   It is.

Citizen 4   Kindly tell the court what you discovered among the prisoner's papers.

Barsad   I discovered lists of His Majesty's forces, together with maps showing their positions.

This 'proof' of treachery causes a
sensation. The spectators boo and hoot.

Citizen 5   Is it your opinion that the prisoner had been in the habit for some years of passing similar information to the King's enemies?

Stryver   (*Standing*) Objection, m'lud!

Citizen 5   I have no further questions.

*The **Citizens** exchange complacent nods*
and sit down.

Stryver   Mr . . . Barsad. Were the documents you so honestly recovered in the prisoner's own handwriting?

Barsad   (*Shiftily*) Could've been.

Stryver   I put it to you that they were not.

Barsad   Well, that proves he's clever, doesn't it? He must've got someone else to copy 'em for him!

There is a buzz of agreement among the
spectators.

Stryver   Mr Barsad, are you now, or have you ever been, a spy?

Barsad   That is a slur on my character.

Judge   Answer the question!

Barsad   I am not.

Stryver   What do you live upon?

Barsad   Private property.

Stryver   And what, or where is this private property?

Barsad   I can't exactly say.

Stryver	Really? Have you ever been to prison, Mr Barsad?
Barsad	Certainly not.
Stryver	Never in a debtors' prison?
Barsad	I don't see what that's got to do with...
Stryver	Never, Mr Barsad?
Barsad	Might've been.
Stryver	And how often? Once? Twice? Three times?
Barsad	About that, yes.
Stryver	Not five or six?
Barsad	Possibly.
Stryver	What *is* your occupation, Mr Barsad?
Barsad	Gentleman.
Stryver	Have you ever been kicked, Mr Barsad?
Barsad	Eh?
Stryver	Come, sir, the question is a simple one. Have you ever been kicked?
Barsad	Might've been.
Stryver	Frequently?
Barsad	No.
Stryver	Ever been kicked downstairs?
Barsad	No! (*Pause*) Well, I once got kicked at the top of some stairs, but I fell down of my own accord.
Stryver	On that occasion, you were accused of cheating at cards?

Barsad	I never! It's a lie!
Stryver	Have you ever borrowed money from the prisoner?
Barsad	(*Reluctantly*) Yes.
Stryver	Did you ever pay him back?
Barsad	No.
Stryver	Mr Barsad, I put it to you that you contrived to force yourself upon the prisoner's company in order to entrap him. I suggest that you never saw the prisoner with these lists, because you procured them yourself as false evidence.

>*The **Citizens** conducting the prosecution stand and object furiously. The spectators applaud and argue. Above all this, **Stryver** thunders his accusation.*

Stryver	I put it to you that you are a paid government spy and informer.
Barsad	(*With great indignation*) It's a lie!
Stryver	No further questions, m'lud. (*He sits*)

>*Barsad leaves the stand and sits with **Lucie** and **Manette** who are not pleased to have his company.*
>*The **Citizens** (except **Citizen 1**) sit down.*

Citizen 1	Call Mr Jarvis Lorry!
Clerk	Mr Jarvis Lorry!

>***Lorry** stands.*

Citizen 1	Mr Lorry, look upon the prisoner. Have you seen him before?
Lorry	I have. Some five years ago, the business of a young client (*He glances at Lucie*) took me to Paris. I met the prisoner aboard the packet ship on the return voyage.

Citizen 7 stands.

Citizen 7	At what hour did the prisoner board the ship?
Lorry	A little after midnight.
Citizen 7	At the dead of night, Mr Lorry. Was he the only passenger to board that ship at such an hour?
Lorry	He happened to be ...
Citizen 7	Never mind 'happened to be', Mr Lorry.
Lorry	He was the only passenger to board at that hour.

Citizens 1 and *7 sit down.* **Lorry** *follows suit.* **Citizen 6** *stands.*

Citizen 6	Doctor Manette.

Manette stands.

Citizen 6	Can you identify the prisoner as your fellow passenger on board a cross-channel packet ship, some five years ago?
Manette	I cannot, sir.
Citizen 6	Is there any special reason why you cannot?

Manette does not reply.

Citizen 6	Was it your misfortune to suffer a long imprisonment, without trial, in your native country?
Manette	A long imprisonment.
Citizen 6	You were newly released on the occasion in question?
Manette	I was. I have no rememberance of the occasion. My mind was a blank for some time following my release.

Citizen 8 stands.

Citizen 8	Then we must seek information elsewhere. Miss Manette!

*Lucie starts, and stands. **Manette** sits.*

Citizen 8	Have you seen the prisoner before?
Lucie	Yes sir, on the packet ship just referred to, on the same occasion.
Citizen 8	Had you any conversation with the prisoner during the crossing?
Lucie	Yes, sir. When the gentleman came on board...
Judge	Do you mean the prisoner?
Lucie	Yes, my lord.
Judge	Then say so!
Lucie	When the prisoner came on board, he noticed that my father was very weak and tired. I wished my father to remain on deck in the fresh air, and the gent...the prisoner was good enough to help me make him comfortable.
Citizen 8	Had the prisoner come on board alone?
Lucie	He arrived with two French gentlemen, who went ashore before we sailed.

*Unnoticed by Lucie, **Carton** pulls at
Lorry's sleeve and whispers to him. **Lorry**
stares at him, then beckons to Stryver.*

Citizen 8	He spoke to these men?
Lucie	Yes.
Citizen 8	Did papers pass between them?
Lucie	I saw them do so.
Citizen 8	Similar to these? (*Holding the papers out for her to see*)

Lucie   Indeed, I don't know.

Citizen 8   And the prisoner's conversation with you, Miss Manette?

Lucie   He was kind, and good, and useful to my father. (*She becomes distressed*) I hope I may not repay him by doing him harm today.

Citizen 8   The conversation, Miss Manette.

Lucie   He told me that he was travelling on business of a delicate nature, which might get people into trouble, and was therefore travelling under an assumed name. He said this business had taken him to France and might take him back and forth between England and France for a long time to come.

Citizen 8   You are aware, Miss Manette, that at this time, the French government was supporting the rebellion in America.

Lucie   I have heard so.

Citizen 8   Did the prisoner mention America to you?

Lucie   He said . . . in a jesting way . . . that perhaps George Washington might gain as great a name in history as King George III.

> *The spectators react furiously to this insult to the King. The **Judge** is scandalized. During this, **Carton** removes his wig and rearranges his hair and costume to look like that worn by **Darnay**, making the resemblance between the two men more noticeable. He stands with his back to the court at large. **Citizens 6 and 8** sit down. **Stryver** stands.*

Stryver   Miss Manette. You are quite certain that the gentleman you saw and spoke with on the packet that night was the prisoner?

Lucie   Quite sure, sir.

Stryver   Did you ever see anyone very like the prisoner?

Lucie   Not so like that I could be mistaken.

Stryver	Look well upon my learned friend here. (*Carton turns*) and then look well upon the prisoner. Are they very like each other?

> *Darnay comes face to face with Carton. Darnay is astonished, Carton amused. Lucie looks from one to the other in confusion.*

Cruncher	Bust me! There's a turn-up.
Spectator	Look at 'em! Like as two peas in a pod.
Stryver	I submit, m'lud, that the only evidence against my client, Mr Charles Darnay, is the unsupported word of a hired spy and traitor. I submit that it is possible, nay likely, that Mr Darnay has been the victim of a case of mistaken identity, and has no case to answer!

> *The spectators chatter in excitement. Lucie sways.*

Carton	Look to that young lady! Don't you see she will fall?

> *Lucie faints. The spectators argue and cheer. The Judge bangs his gavel.*

Judge	(*Shouting above the noise*) Case dismissed!

> *The Citizens furiously accuse Barsad of weakening their case. Barsad protests that their losing the case is not his fault. They pursue him out of court. The Judge leaves. The court empties as the Clerk of the Court clears unruly spectators. Others help Manette and Stryver bear Lucie away. Lorry turns to Cruncher.*

Lorry	Jerry! Message to Tellson's! The word is, 'Acquitted'.
Cruncher	If you'd said, 'Recalled to life' again, sir, I should have known what you meant this time.

*Cruncher hurries out. Lorry follows
Stryver. Darnay is alone and looks around
him in confusion. Carton emerges from the
shadows.*

Carton   This is an odd chance that throws you and me together. A strange world, is it not? Or perhaps, as you've just escaped being sent to another world, you feel more kindly disposed to this one. Drink this.

*Carton offers Darnay a flask. Darnay
drinks from it and hands it back to
Carton.*

Carton   There, do you feel life returning?

Darnay   I'm beginning to feel I belong in this world again.

Carton   That must be an immense satisfaction to you. My greatest desire is to forget that I belong in it. It has no good in it for me... except for this (*He lifts his flask ironically to toast Darnay*) ... nor I for it. So we are not much alike in that particular – or in any other, I think. (*He hands the flask back to Darnay*) Come, Mr Darnay, you must propose a toast.

Darnay   Well then... the toast is – Miss Manette!

*Darnay drinks and passes the flask to
Carton.*

Carton   Miss Manette, then. That's a fine young lady to be pitied by and wept for by. How does it feel? Is it worth being tried for one's life, to be the object of such sympathy and compassion, Mr Darnay?

Darnay   I must thank you for your intervention in my trial today...

Carton   I neither want nor deserve your thanks. What I did required no effort on my part, and I don't know why I did it. I suppose you think I'm drunk?

Darnay   I think you have been drinking.

Carton	I think you're right. It would be astonishing if you were not right. I am often drunk. Do you think I like you, Mr Darnay?
Darnay	You have acted as a friend; but I don't think you do.
Carton	*I* don't think I do. I care for no man on earth, and no man on earth cares for me.
Darnay	I think I had better pay my respects to Miss Manette, and see if she is recovered. If you will excuse me, Mr ...
Carton	Carton. Sydney Carton.
Darnay	Mr Carton.

Darnay exits.

Carton	Why should I like a man who looks like me? There is nothing in me to like. A good reason to talk to a man, Carton, that he shows you what you might have been. Change places, and would she have looked at you as she looked at him? Be honest with yourself Carton; you hate the fellow.

Stryver enters.

Stryver	Whom do you hate?
Carton	Our client, just acquitted.
Stryver	Oh? And why?
Carton	When I looked at him, I thought I might have been much the same sort of fellow, if I'd had any luck.
Stryver	That's what put you on to the resemblance, eh? Well, it was useful, very useful ... but don't go around hating your clients, m'dear fellow, it's bad for business. You did sound work today though, on that prosecution witness; every question hit Mr John Barsad where it hurt.
Carton	I always am sound, am I not?
Stryver	Always, my dear fellow! Here are tomorrow's papers.

Carton	Can you explain why it falls to me to sift the papers, and prepare the case; and to you to lead the case and receive the fame? Even when we were starving students in Paris, you were always somewhere, and I . . . nowhere.
Stryver	Old Seesaw Sydney. Up one minute and down the next. (*He neatly takes Carton's flask*) Cheer up, man! A toast – the pretty witness!
Carton	Which pretty witness?
Stryver	The picturesque doctor's daughter, Miss Manette.
Carton	*She* pretty?
Stryver	Is she not?
Carton	She's a golden-haired doll.
Stryver	Do you know, Sydney, I rather thought at the time that you were quite taken with the golden-haired doll.

*Darnay returns with **Manette**, **Lucie**, **Lorry**, and **Cruncher**.*

Lorry	Jerry, summon a cab if you please. I fear we are in for a storm.
Manette	The first drops are falling now. It comes slowly.
Carton	It comes surely.

The others notice Carton and Stryver for the first time. There is an awkward pause.

Lorry	Stryver, my dear fellow . . .

***Lorry** engages **Stryver** in conversation.*

Carton	I trust you are recovered, Miss Manette.
Lucie	I am quite recovered, thank you.

*The others are silent. **Lucie** smiles shyly at Carton. In the shadows, the **Citizens** enter and begin to make the sound of footsteps.*

Lucie   How strange. I hear people hurrying to find shelter before the storm breaks; yet there is no one to be seen.

Darnay   So many people, yet not a soul to be seen.

Lucie   You will think me foolish; but just now those echoes seemed to be the echoes of all the footsteps that are by and by coming into our lives.

*The **Citizens**, in shadow, increase the noise of their footsteps and begin to press in upon the small group.*

Carton   There is a great crowd coming into our lives one day, if that is so.

Darnay   Are all these footsteps destined to come to all of us, Miss Manette?

Lucie   I imagined them the footsteps of the people who are to come into my life, and my father's.

Carton   I take them into mine! There is a great crowd bearing down upon us, Miss Manette; I see them – by the lightening! And I hear them! Here they come, fast, fierce, and furious.

*The storm breaks. Just as the **Citizens** are about to surround the group, **Cruncher** enters carrying an umbrella and beckons to Manette and Lucie.*

Cruncher   Cab's waiting, doctor . . . miss.

*The **Citizens** retreat into shadow. **Lucie** helps **Manette** off towards the cab. **Cruncher** goes with them sheltering them with the umbrella. **Stryver** bids **Lorry** good night and vanishes back into the court. **Cruncher** returns with the umbrella.*

Lorry   Almost a night, Jerry, to bring the dead out of their graves.

Cruncher   I never seen the night myself, that would do that.

Lorry   Good night, Mr Carton. Good night, Mr Darnay. Shall we ever see such a night again, together?

> *Lorry exits with **Cruncher**. **Carton** strides out into the storm. **Darnay** watches him go.*
> *Lights down.*

Scene 2

> *The lights go up on the raised upstage area. The **Marquis** enters. The **Citizens** enter and surround him. Downstage, in darkness the Marquis' carriage is prepared, and his **driver** awaits him.*

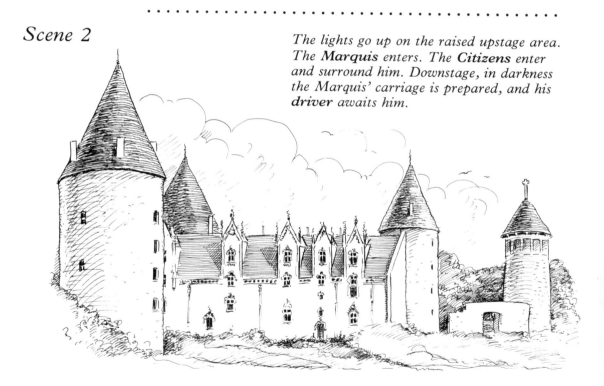

Citizen 5   Some weeks later...

Citizen 6   ...in Paris...

Citizen 5   ...monseigneur is about to take his chocolate.

Citizen 6	Monseigneur can swallow a great many things with ease.
Citizen 5	He swallows, for instance, the taxes of the poor, sentencing them to misery, starvation and death...
Citizen 6	...but he is incapable of swallowing his chocolate without the aid of four strong men.

*Four **lackeys** enter and play out the scene as described.*

Citizen 1	The first lackey carries the chocolate pot into the sacred presence.
Citizen 2	The second mills and froths the chocolate with the little instrument he carries for that purpose.
Citizen 3	The third presents monseigneur with his napkin...
Citizen 4	...and the chief lackey pours the chocolate out.
Citizen 6	It would be impossible for monseigneur to dispense with one of these attendants.
Citizen 5	Deep would have been his shame had he been waited on by only three men...
Citizen 6	...to have been waited on by two, would have killed him.

*The fawning **chief lackey** presents the chocolate to the **Marquis**, who dashes it from his hands. The **lackeys** cower.*

Citizen 7	Monseigneur is displeased.
Citizen 8	His wealth evaporates.
Citizen 7	He is frowned upon by the great men at court.
Citizen 8	He is low in fortune and out of favour.
Citizen 1	Monseigneur orders his carriage.

*The **lackeys** exit.*
*Lights up on the carriage. The **Marquis** descends and enters the carriage. The **Citizens** follow him and take up a position downstage. The **driver** mounts. We hear the rattle of the carriage as it starts and speeds up. The lights on the carriage dim. Only the **Citizens** can be seen.*

Citizen 2   He orders his driver to whip up the horses...

Citizen 3   ...and the man obeys.

Citizen 4   The carriage tears through the narrow streets...

Citizen 5   ...the crowded streets...

Citizen 6   ...where citizens scream and flee the mad charge of the plunging horses and clattering carriage of monseigneur...

Citizen 1   ...until...

*There is a break in the rhythm of the carriage. A scream rings out. It is taken up by many voices. Enter a crowd, including **Gaspard**. A huddled shape lies downstage. **Gaspard** howls and weeps over it. The lights come up. The **Marquis** alights from the carriage. The **Citizens** rush to join the crowd. Angry people reach for the **driver** who fends them off with his whip.*

Marquis   Driver! There was a jolt. What has gone wrong?

*The crowd draws back. The frightened **driver** gestures with his whip.*

Citizen 1   (*Humbly*) Pardon, Monsieur the Marquis, it is a child.

Marquis   (*Indicating Gaspard*) Why does he make that abominable noise? Is it his child?

Citizen 1   Excuse me, Monsieur the Marquis...it is a pity...yes.

Gaspard rises and appears to threaten the Marquis, who puts his hand to his sword.

Gaspard   Killed!

Gaspard throws himself on the body of the child and howls again.
The Marquis takes out his purse.

Marquis   It is extraordinary to me that you people cannot take care of yourselves and your children. One or the other of you is forever in the way. How do I know what injury you have done my horses? (*He throws a coin down*) Give him that.

The crowd mutter. Defarge enters. He goes to Gaspard. Mme Defarge enters. She takes no part in the scene but sits aside and composedly, knits.

Defarge   I know all, I know all. Be a brave man, my Gaspard. It is better for the poor little plaything to die so, than to live. It has died in a moment without pain. Could it have lived an hour as happily?

Marquis   You are a philosopher, you there. How do they call you?

Defarge   They call me Defarge.

Marquis   Of what trade?

Defarge   Monsieur the Marquis, vendor of wine.

Marquis   (*Throwing down another coin*) Pick that up, philosopher and vendor of wine, and spend it as you will. (*Turning*) The horses there, are they all right?

Defarge picks up the coin, spits on it, and throws it at the Marquis. He steps back and the crowd closes, hiding him from view.

Marquis   Who threw that?

> *There is no response. The crowd draws back. The* **Citizens** *return to their previous position downstage.*

Marquis   You dogs. I would ride my carriage over any of you very willingly, and exterminate you from the earth.

> *The* **Marquis'** *gaze locks with* **Mme Defarge**, *who carries on knitting. The* **Marquis** *is discomfitted. He turns and mounts his carriage.*

Marquis   Drive on!

> *The lights fade except for tight spots on the Citizens.*

Citizen 8   The Marquis drives on.

Citizen 7   He is satisfied...

Citizen 6   ...as one who has accidentally broken some common thing...

Citizen 5   ...and paid for it.

Citizen 4   He has outfaced the mob.

Citizen 3   Now, he arrives at his country estate...

Citizen 2   ...at the village, poor and miserable, that lies in the very shadow of the great walls of his château.

Citizen 1   The people of the village are ragged.

Citizen 3   There are few children...

Citizen 4   ...and no dogs.

> *The other* **Citizens** *look at Citizen 4 as if to ask 'why?'.* **Citizen 4** *mimes eating. The* **Citizens** *nod glumly to indicate their understanding.*

Citizen 5	Nobody is in the village square to welcome the Marquis home...
Citizen 6	...except the Marquis' servant, Gabelle...
Citizen 7	...a handful of starving peasants...
Citizen 5	...and a mender of roads.

> *Lights up on **Gabelle**, a **roadmender**, and a group of peasants. The **Citizens** join the crowd. The **Marquis**, standing by his carriage, looks up as the **roadmender** mooches across the stage.*

Marquis	Gabelle! Bring that fellow here.

> ***Gabelle** obeys.*

Marquis	I passed you on the road.
Roadmender	Marquis, it is true.
Marquis	What were you staring at as I passed you?

> *The **roadmender** is a slow thinker and all his answers take time.*

Roadmender	Monseigneur, at the man.

> *The **roadmender** points under the carriage.*

Marquis	What man, pig?
Roadmender	Pardon, monseigneur, he hung from that chain there.
Marquis	Who?
Roadmender	Monseigneur, the man.
Marquis	May the Devil carry away these idiots! What man? Who was he?

Roadmender I am sorry, monseigneur, he was a stranger.

Marquis He was swinging beneath the carriage?

Roadmender Indeed, monseigneur. His head hung like this...

> *The **roadmender** demonstrates. His cap falls off. He recovers it and bows.*

Roadmender ... he was all white with dust, white as a ghost!

Marquis Gabelle! Send him away.

Gabelle On your way, fellow.

Marquis I want you to keep an eye out for this stranger, Gabelle. If he seeks lodging in the village, arrest him and find out his business.

Gabelle Monseigneur, I am flattered to devote myself to your orders.

Marquis Did the man run away, fellow... where is the fool?

> *The **roadmender** is showing the group of peasants how the man hung beneath the Marquis' carriage.*

Marquis Did the man run away, dolt, when we stopped to skid the wheels?

Roadmender Monseigneur, he threw himself over the hillside, as one would dive into the river.

Marquis Gabelle, I want this man found.

> *The **Marquis** mounts his carriage impatiently. **Gabelle**, the **roadmender** and the peasants glide backwards* to give the impression that the carriage is moving. The lights dim until only the **Citizens** are visible.*

Citizen 3 Monseigneur arrives.

Citizen 4	The great door of his château is opened to him.
Citizen 2	The lights of flambeaux greet him.
Citizen 1	Monseigneur has a visitor.

*The lights come up on the Marquis' apartment. A chair and a table with candles have been set. **Darnay** stands waiting. The **Marquis** enters with **Gabelle**. He stops short on seeing Darnay, then hands his hat and gloves to **Gabelle**, who exits.*

Marquis	Good evening, nephew.
Darnay	You left Paris yesterday, sir?
Marquis	Yesterday. I expected you earlier.
Darnay	I was . . . detained.
Marquis	Dear me.
Darnay	I think you are quite aware of my recent arrest and trial in London. For anything I know, you may have been responsible for it.
Marquis	(*Ironically*) You do me too much honour.
Darnay	You would stop at nothing to prevent me from doing what I have set out to do.
Marquis	My friend, I told you so long ago.
Darnay	Indeed, were you not out of favour at court, I believe a little note from you would have sent me to rot in some fortress indefinitely.
Marquis	Once, perhaps. From this room, many insolent dogs were taken out to be hanged. In my bedroom next door, one fellow, to our knowledge, was spitted by a dagger for complaining about some indelicacy respecting his daughter. France has changed,

my boy. We have lost many privileges. Such gentle aids to the power and honour of families are seldom to be had nowadays. Otherwise, for the honour of the family, I could even resolve to make things inconvenient for you to that extent. Pray excuse me!

Darnay At any rate, I know you would stop me renouncing the property at all costs.

Marquis The property is not yet yours to renounce, nephew.

Darnay If it were to pass from you to me tomorrow...

Marquis Which I have the vanity to hope is not probable.

Darnay ...I would abandon it, and live otherwise and elsewhere. What is it but a wilderness of misery and ruin? A crumbling tower of waste, mismanagement, extortion, debt, oppression, hunger, nakedness and suffering?

>   *The* **Marquis** *makes no reply, but smiles in satisfaction.*

Darnay I intend to free it for the use and benefit of the miserable people whom we have wronged.

Marquis Whom *we* have wronged?

Darnay Our honourable family has done a world of wrong, injuring every human creature who came between us and our pleasure. First my father, then you. I am your heir, bound to a system that is frightful to me and powerless to change it.

Marquis And how... forgive my curiosity... do you graciously intend to live when you have so nobly renounced the family name and fortune?

Darnay As many, even of noble birth, will have to do one day: work.

Marquis In England, for example?

Darnay Yes. You need have no fear of the family name, sir. I do not use it in England.

Marquis	You are ashamed of our family name?
Darnay	Our family has used its power with such cruelty that I believe our name to be more detested than any name in France.
Marquis	Let us hope so. The more we are hated, the greater our power.

*The **Marquis** starts suddenly and looks off stage.*

Marquis	What is that?
Darnay	What?
Marquis	Outside the blinds. Open the blinds.

__Darnay__ 'opens the blinds'.

Darnay	I see nothing. Only trees, and the night.
Marquis	Very well. Close them again.

__Darnay__ does so.

Marquis	Repression, my friend, is our only hope of survival. Fear will keep the dogs obedient to the whip as long as this roof shuts out the sky.
Darnay	I seek only justice for our people.
Marquis	If you seek it from me, my nephew, you will for ever seek it in vain, be assured. My friend, I will die, perpetuating the system under which I have lived.

*The **Marquis** rings for Gabelle.*

Darnay	Shall I bid you goodnight, sir?
Marquis	(*Turning*) You know a compatriot of ours who, I hear, has found refuge in England? A doctor?
Darnay	Yes.

Marquis   With a daughter?

Darnay   Yes.

Marquis   Yes. A doctor with a daughter. France has indeed changed. You are fatigued. Good night.

> *Gabelle enters.*

Marquis   Gabelle, light monsieur my nephew to his chamber . . .

> *Gabelle leads Darnay out.*

Marquis   . . . and burn monsieur my nephew in his bed, if you will.

> *The Marquis snuffs all but one candle and sits. The lights dim.*
> *A shadowy figure (Gaspard) enters and moves behind the Marquis' chair.*
> *Gaspard's face appears next to the Marquis', and his knife appears at the Marquis' throat.*

Gaspard   Monseigneur, my daughter wished me to say . . . good night.

> *The Marquis screams. Gaspard 'cuts his throat', then snuffs out the last candle flame. In the darkness, Gaspard attaches a note to the Marquis' coat and exits.*
> *Darnay enters with a light.*

Darnay   Uncle? What is it? What's wro . . .

> *He sees the wound.*

Darnay   My God! Gabelle! Gabelle! Lights!

> *Gabelle enters and gazes horrified at the Marquis.*

Darnay   Who has done this?

Gabelle   Monsieur Charles, there is a note.

*Darnay takes the note from the Marquis'
coat, and reads it.*

Darnay　　　'Drive him fast to his tomb. This, from ... Jacques.'

Gabelle　　　(*Clears his throat*) What would you have us do? ... Monsieur
　　　　　　　the Marquis.

*Darnay turns to Gabelle in shock as his
use of the title registers.
Dead blackout.*

Scene 3　　　*Lights up on the **Citizens** standing in their
　　　　　　　downstage position as before.*

Citizen 3　　　Some years have passed.

Citizen 5　　　Charles Darnay has renounced his title, and that other name
　　　　　　　which he does not use in England.

Citizen 7　　　He is settled in London, and for part of the year teaches
　　　　　　　French at Cambridge.

*The lights brighten to reveal **Manette** at
work in his study.*

Citizen 1   He frequently visits Doctor Manette and Lucie. The doctor is almost recovered from his long imprisonment.

> *Manette stops work, and raises to his head a hand that trembles slightly. He shakes his head and is himself again.*

Citizen 3   Almost... but not quite.

> *The **Citizens** exit quietly as **Darnay** enters.*

Manette   Charles Darnay! I rejoice to see you! Sydney Carton led us to expect you three or four days ago.

Darnay   (*Without enthusiasm*) I am obliged to Mr Carton for his interest in the matter. Miss Manette... (*He stops short*)

Manette   My daughter has stepped out with Miss Pross...

Darnay   Doctor Manette, I knew she was from home. I took the opportunity of her being from home, to beg to speak to you.

> *Manette indicates a chair near his own.*
> *Darnay sits down.*

Darnay   Doctor Manette, I hope the subject I am about to touch upon may not...

Manette   Is Lucie the topic?

Darnay   She is.

Manette   I find it hard to speak of her. I find it harder to listen when you speak so of her. What do you wish to say?

Darnay   That I admire your daughter, Doctor Manette. That I am devoted to her. That, if ever there were love in the world, I love her.

> *There is a silence.*

Manette   I believe it. I do you justice; I believe it.

Darnay	You have loved, yourself. Let your old love speak for me.
Manette	(*With sudden passion*) Not that, sir! You must not speak of that!

Darnay is puzzled and remains silent. Manette becomes calmer.

Manette	I ask your pardon. I do not doubt your loving Lucie. (*Pause*) Have you ever spoken to her?

Darnay shakes his head.

Manette	Or written?
Darnay	Never.
Manette	You have remained silent out of consideration for me. I thank you.
Darnay	I have forborne as long as it is in the nature of man to do it. But, as Heaven is my witness, I love her.
Manette	(*Nods*) I have thought so before now.
Darnay	I beg you to believe that, if I am to be so fortunate as to make Lucie my wife, I should never at any time seek to put any separation between you. I look only, as a fellow-exile, to share your fortunes and be faithful to you both, to the death.
Manette	Have you any reason to believe that Lucie loves you?
Darnay	As yet, none.
Manette	Do you seek any promise from me?
Darnay	I well understand that, without you, I could have no hope. I understand also that a word from you in my favour would guarantee my happiness. For which reason, Doctor Manette, I would not ask that word, to save my life.
Manette	I am sure of it.

Darnay	Yet, I do ask a promise. If Lucie should seek your advice, I hope you will tell her what I have just said, and that you believe it; and that you will not influence her against me.
Manette	I will promise this: if she tells me that you are the man she has chosen as her husband, I shall give her to you. If . . . if I were to imagine any reasons, any apprehensions, anything whatsoever against the man she really loved, short of his direct responsibility . . . I should forget them all for her sake.
Darnay	I hardly understand you, sir.
Manette	She is everything to me; more to me than suffering, than wrong, than . . . Well! This is idle talk. (*He is clearly disturbed*) What was it you said to me?
Darnay	I thank you for your confidence in me, and wish to return it with full confidence on my part. The name 'Darnay' is not my own. I wish to tell you my reason for being in England. I wish you to know my true name.
Manette	Stop!
Darnay	I wish it, that I may deserve your confidence and have no secrets from you.
Manette	Stop!

Manette stops his ears with his fingers.

Manette	Tell me when I ask you, not now. If Lucie returns your love, you shall tell me on your marriage morning. Do you promise?
Darnay	Willingly.
Manette	Then, give me your hand. She will be home directly, and it is better she should not see us together tonight.
Darnay	May I wait in the garden until Miss Lucie returns?
Manette	Wait? Yes, If you will. If you must. But for now, please go! God bless you!

Darnay rises and shakes Manette's hand in some confusion. He leaves. As Manette watches him go, something of his old manner returns.

Manette   Where did I put them? So much to do...

Manette seems like an old man again, tired and confused. He leaves the stage. Almost immediately, Lucie enters from the other side.

Lucie   Father? Where are you?

Miss Pross enters.

Lucie   Miss Pross, have you seen my father?

Miss Pross   He was in here. I thought your Mr Darnay was with him.

Lucie   My Mr Darnay?

Miss Pross   Huh!

Lucie   Don't you like Mr Darnay, Nana Pross?

Miss Pross   I don't want dozens of people who are not at all worthy of Ladybird to come here looking after her.

Lucie   And do dozens of people come for that purpose?

Miss Pross   Hundreds! There never was, or will be, but one man worthy of Ladybird; and that was my brother Solomon, if he hadn't made a mistake in life.

There is a knock from off stage.

Miss Pross   You see? Hundreds of people!

Miss Pross goes off and returns ushering in Sydney Carton. He looks ill, and uneasy.

Miss Pross	Mr Sydney Carton. (*Having made her point*) Hah!

She sweeps out.

Lucie	Mr Carton. I fear you are not well.
Carton	No. The life I lead, Miss Manette, is not a healthy one.
Lucie	Is it not – forgive me – is it not a pity to lead no better life?
Carton	God knows it is a shame!
Lucie	Then why not change it?
Carton	It is too late for that. I shall never be better than I am; I shall sink lower, and be worse.

Carton covers his eyes with his hands.

Carton	Pray forgive me. I have something to say to you. Will you hear me?
Lucie	If it will make you happier, I shall be glad to hear it.
Carton	Don't be afraid to hear me. I am like one who died young. All my life might have been.
Lucie	I am sure that the best part of it might still be.
Carton	I know better; even though I wish with all my heart that I might be worthy of you.

Lucie is very disturbed, and makes to move away from him.

Carton	I know that you could never return the love of a man such as myself: a wasted, drunken, poor creature. Even if you could feel some tenderness towards me, I know that I should bring you to misery, sorrow and repentance. I do not ask you to love me. I am thankful that you cannot.
Lucie	If I cannot love you, Mr Carton, can I not help you to save yourself?

Carton	I fear not. If you will hear me through a very little more, all you can ever do for me is done. Knowing you has stirred old shadows that I thought had died out in me: guilt, remorse, the knowledge of what I might have been. You started a fire in me; but the flames flicker and die, providing no light, doing no service, idly burning away.
Lucie	I am sorry to have made you more unhappy than you were before you knew me . . .
Carton	Don't say that, Miss Manette. Nobody else in the world could have persuaded me to change my ways. I have spoken to you like this for one reason only: that for the rest of my misdirected life, I may remember that I opened my heart to you, before I sank so low as to be unworthy of your pity.

Lucie is increasingly upset. Off stage, a sound of tapping begins. It is not loud, but it persists quietly through the remainder of the scene.

Carton	I distress you; I have little more to say. Please let me believe that you will share this confidence with no one.
Lucie	The secret is yours, Mr Carton, not mine, and I promise to respect it.
Carton	Thank you, and God bless you. I shall never refer to this conversation again; but at the hour of my death, I shall know that one person at least will remember my name, and know my faults, and still feel pity at my passing.

Lucie begins to weep.

Carton	Be comforted. I am not worth such feeling, Miss Manette. The next time you see me, I shall be the degraded wretch you have always known; but you will know that my true feelings towards you will never change. I beg you to believe this of me.
Lucie	I do, Mr Carton.

Carton	Believe one thing more of me; I would do anything, embrace any sacrifice for you, and for those dear to you, if it were to cost me my life. Once again, God bless you...(*He kisses her hand*)...and farewell.

> *Carton* exits, almost colliding with *Darnay* as he does. They bow formally, but *Darnay* is displeased to see Carton. He enters the room and realizes that *Lucie* has been crying.

Darnay   Miss Manette...Lucie...has that fellow been upsetting you?

Lucie   Please, you must not ask me that.

Darnay   But...

Lucie   Dear Mr Darnay, please let me ask something of you instead.

Darnay   You have only to name it.

Lucie   I wish to ask you to treat poor Mr Carton with more consideration than you have in the past.

Darnay   Since you ask it...but why?

Lucie   That is what you are not to ask me. But for my sake, please be generous with him; he is miserably unhappy. He has a heart that he very, very seldom reveals, and there are deep wounds in it. Yet I am sure he is capable of goodness, gentleness, even self-sacrifice.

Darnay   If I have misjudged him, I am sorry for it. I never intended him any injury.

Lucie   I know. Thank you.

Darnay   Miss Manette, I in my turn have something to ask you... though it is an infinitely greater request than yours regarding Mr Carton. I may only hope that you can find it in your heart to grant it.

He steels himself.

Darnay	Miss Manette...

> *Miss Pross bursts in, distraught. The noise of tapping is much louder.*

Miss Pross	Oh, my lamb...oh, my ladybird...
Lucie	Miss Pross, what is it?
Miss Pross	Oh, come quick, miss – Mr Darnay, you too – oh miss, your father...
Lucie	My father? What's the matter?
Miss Pross	Oh, miss...he doesn't know me. And he's making shoes...

> *Lucie and Darnay exchange a horrified glance and rush out. Miss Pross follows. Lights dim. Citizens 2, 4, 6 and 8 enter downstage and speak during the scene change.*

Citizen 2	Doctor Manette's relapse is brief; under his daughter's gentle care, he soon recovers.
Citizen 4	Charles Darnay makes his proposal.
Citizen 6	His proposal is accepted.
Citizen 4	Wedding plans are made.
Citizen 6	The sun shines on Lucie Manette and her betrothed, Charles Darnay.
Citizen 8	But in Paris, stormclouds are gathering.

· ·

Scene 4

The lights come up on the Defarges' wine shop. **Mme Defarge** *sits behind the counter and knits.* **The Vengeance** *sits near her.* **Jacques 2, 3 and 4,** *whom we last saw observing Doctor Manette through the keyhole of his attic door, are present, drinking little and saying less. They are joined by* **Citizens 2, 4, 6 and 8.** **Defarge** *enters with the* **roadmender.** **The Vengeance** *immediately goes to the door to keep watch.*

Defarge   Good day!

Customers   Good day.

Defarge   This is the man I met by arrangement a day and a half's journey out of Paris. He is a good child, a mender of roads, called Jacques. Give him a drink, my wife!

Mme Defarge pours wine for the roadmender. Catching Defarge's eye, she nods. Defarge looks outside, then takes the roadmender over to join the others.

Defarge   Jacques Two, Jacques Three, Jacques Four! This is the witness, Jacques Five. He will tell you all. Speak, Jacques!

The roadmender is bashful.

Jacques 2   Jacques One (*He indicates Defarge*) has told us how you saw our friend Gaspard hanging from the Marquis' carriage, and how the Marquis questioned you ...

Roadmender   (*Frightened*) I told Monsieur the Marquis nothing. My faith! Nothing!

Jacques 3   Good. Do not be afraid. We know that, having taken his revenge, Gaspard remained hidden for many months, but was at last, unluckily, found. Go on from there.

Roadmender	Then, messieurs, here is what passed. I am again at work on the hillside when I raise my eyes and see six soldiers driving before them a tall man with his arms tied to his sides . . . like this. (*He demonstrates*) I recognize the tall man; and he recognizes me, but neither of us gives any sign. He wishes now he could throw himself over the hillside, as on the evening when I first saw him, in that very spot. 'Come on,' cries the chief of the soldiers, 'bring him fast to his tomb!' They drive him with their guns, like this! (*He demonstrates*) He falls. His face bleeds, but he is bound, he cannot touch it. The soldiers laugh.
Defarge	Go on, Jacques.
Roadmender	They put him in a lofty iron cage. I see him as I go to work the next day, hanging high over the walls, looking through the bars. He is still bound. He cannot wave to me. I dare not call to him. He regards me like a dead man. He remains in the cage for some days. There are rumours in the village that a petition has been presented in Paris, showing that he was enraged and made mad by the death of his child; they say that this petition has been presented to the King himself.
Jacques 4	Listen, then, Jacques. Know that a petition was presented to the King and Queen. It was Defarge whom you see here who, at the hazard of his life, darted before the horses with the petition in his hand.
Jacques 3	And once again, listen, Jacques. The guards surrounded Defarge then, and struck him blows. You hear?
Defarge	Enough! Long live the Devil! Go on.
Roadmender	On Sunday night, when all the village is asleep, soldiers come from the prison. Their guns ring on the stones of the little street. Workmen dig, workmen hammer, soldiers laugh and sing; in the morning, by the fountain, there is raised a gallows forty feet high. All work is stopped, all assemble. Nobody leads the cows out, the cows are there with the rest. At midday, the roll of drums. The prisoner appears, in the midst of many soldiers. He is bound as before, and in his mouth is a gag – tied so, with a tight string, making him look almost as if he laughed. (*He demonstrates*) On the top of the gallows is fixed

the knife, blade upwards with its point in the air. He is hanged there, forty feet high . . . and is left hanging, poisoning the water. When I left the village, as the sun was going to bed, and looked back from the hill, the shadow struck across the church, across the prison . . . seemed to strike across the earth, messieurs, to where the sky rests upon it.

There is a silence.

Jacques 2   Good! You have acted and recounted faithfully, Jacques. Will you wait for us a little, within there?

> *The **roadmender** is shown into the inner room off stage. **Mme Defarge** stops her knitting and gazes questioningly at her husband.*

Jacques 4   How say you, Jacques? To be registered?

Defarge   To be registered, as doomed to destruction.

Jacques 3   The château, and all who bear the name of the Marquis?

Defarge   The château, and all who bear that name. Extermination!

The Vengeance   (*From her position at the door*) Magnificent!

> *The **Vengeance** bites her fingers in excitement. **Mme Defarge** nods contentedly.*

Mme Defarge   Soon, my Vengeance. Very soon.

> *She begins to knit.*

Jacques 3   Are you sure it is safe, to keep the names of the condemned in such a manner? To be sure, no one besides ourselves can decipher the register, but will madame always be able to do so herself?

Defarge	It would be easier for the weakest poltroon that lives to erase himself from existence, than to erase one letter of his **name** or crimes from the knitted register of Madame Defarge. I have another name for your register, my dear. A name given to me by Jacques of the police. There is another spy commissioned for our quarter. There may be more, but he knows of one. He is English.
Mme Defarge	So much the better. His name?

The Vengeance, however, whistles before Defarge can give the name. **Mme Defarge** *pins a rose to her head-dress.* **Defarge** *ducks into the inner room off stage.* **The Vengeance** *saunters into the wine shop, and the three* **Jacques** *lounge innocently.*
John Barsad *enters the wine shop. Over the next few speeches, the* **Citizens,** *the* **Jacques** *and* **The Vengeance** *quietly finish their drinks and leave the shop.*

Barsad	Good day, madame.
Mme Defarge	Good day, monsieur.
Barsad	A glass of old cognac, if you please, madame.

Mme Defarge *pours the drink.* **Barsad** *attempts to nod to the customers who remain; they cold-shoulder him.*

Barsad	(*Drinking*) Ah! Marvellous cognac, this!

A **Jacques** *who is about to leave exchanges an astonished glance with* **Mme Defarge,** *and goes.*

Mme Defarge	The cognac is flattered, monsieur.
Barsad	You knit with great skill, madame.
Mme Defarge	I am accustomed to it.
Barsad	A pretty pattern, too. May one ask what it is for?
Mme Defarge	Pastime only. I may find a use for it one day. If I do, well – I'll use it!

> *Customer 1* and *Customer 2* enter on the opposite side of the stage. *Customer 1* is prevented by *Customer 2* from entering the shop.

Customer 1	What are you doing? I am thirsty!
Customer 2	Imbecile! Do you not see madame's rose? There are spies about!

> *Customers 1* and *2* turn and go, unnoticed by Barsad.

Barsad	You have a husband, madame?
Mme Defarge	I have.
Barsad	Children?
Mme Defarge	No children.
Barsad	Business is bad?
Mme Defarge	Very bad. The people are so poor.
Barsad	So oppressed, too – as you say.
Mme Defarge	As *you* say.
Barsad	Pardon me, it was certainly I who said so, but you naturally think so. Of course.

Mme Defarge	I and my husband have enough to do to keep this wine shop open, without thinking.

Barsad is making nothing of this, and tries another tack.

Barsad	A bad business, this, of Gaspard's execution. Ah! The poor Gaspard.
Mme Defarge	My faith! If people use knives for such purposes, they have to pay for it.
Barsad	I believe there is much compassion and anger in this neighbourhood, touching the poor fellow? Between ourselves?
Mme Defarge	Is there? . . . here is my husband.

Defarge enters.

Barsad	Good day, Jacques!

Defarge stares at Barsard.

Barsad	(*With less conviction*) Good day, Jacques!
Defarge	You mistake me for another, monsieur. I am Ernest Defarge.
Barsad	(*Uncomfortably*) It is all the same. Good day.
Defarge	Good day.
Barsad	I was saying to madame, that they tell me there is much sympathy and anger in Saint-Antoine, touching the unhappy fate of poor Gaspard.
Defarge	No one has told me so. I know nothing of it.
Barsad	(*Changing the subject*) I am sure your name is familiar to me, Monsieur Defarge.
Defarge	Indeed.

Barsad   Yes, indeed. When Doctor Manette was released, you, his old domestic, had the charge of him. You see I am informed as to the circumstances?

Defarge   Such is the fact, certainly.

Barsad   It was to you that his daughter came; and it was from your care that she took him, accompanied by a neat brown monsieur; how is he called? Lorry – of Tellson's Bank, in England.

Defarge   Such is the fact.

Barsad   I have known Doctor Manette, and his daughter, in England.

Defarge   Yes?

Barsad   You don't hear much about them now?

Mme Defarge   In effect, nothing.

Barsad   Then it will surprise you that she is going to be married.

Mme Defarge   Going to be? (*She sniffs*) She might have been married long ago. You English are cold, it seems to me.

Barsad   Oh! You know I am English?

Mme Defarge   I hear your tongue is. What the tongue is, I suppose the man is.

Barsad   (*Laughing nervously*) Yes, Miss Manette is to be married; but not to an Englishman; to one who is, like herself, French by birth. And speaking of Gaspard (ah, poor Gaspard! It was cruel, cruel) it is a curious thing that she is going to marry the nephew of Monsieur the Marquis, for whose death Gaspard was hanged; in other words, the present marquis. But he lives unknown in England, he is no marquis there; he is Mr Charles Darnay. D'Aulnais is the name of his mother's family. Good day to you.

> *Barsard goes. Defarge checks that he has really departed. Mme Defarge takes the rose from her head-dress.*

Defarge　　Can it be true? What he said of Ma'amselle Manette?

Mme Defarge　　As *he* has said it, it is probably false. But it may be true.

Defarge　　If it is, I hope for her sake that her husband's destiny may keep him out of France.

Mme Defarge　　Her husband's destiny will take him where it will. I wish the name of that spy.

Defarge　　His name is John Barsad.

Mme Defarge　　(*Knitting*) So.

Defarge　　You have his name?

Mme Defarge　　I have both names; the spy's, and that of Monsieur Darnay.

> *Dead blackout.*

· ·

Scene 5

> *The scene contains two centres of action. Upstage, Defarge and Mme Defarge lead the storming of the Bastille. In one of the downstage areas, the wedding of Lucie Manette and Charles Darnay is staged. Lights up downstage. Darnay is waiting alone. Lorry enters in a great hurry.*

Lorry　　Darnay, my dear fellow, my most heartfelt apologies. To be late, today of all days!

Darnay　　I had almost given you up, Mr Lorry.

Lorry　　Business, my friend, business. I began to think I should never get away from Tellson's. There is much uneasiness in Paris; our French customers are sending us their property as fast as ships can carry it over the channel.

Darnay   This has a bad look.

Lorry   Eh? Oh, well, you may say so. Something is about to happen in Paris, Darnay. Do you recall the night of your acquittal, when we stood before the Old Bailey, and heard a multitude of hurrying footsteps, and saw the lightning? At my desk in London today, I heard wild footsteps and saw terrible lightning flash in the skies over that other city. I thank God no friends of mine are in Paris today... (**Darnay** *looks troubled*) ...but enough of this, your bride is arriving. Now then, dear boy, business, merely business.

The wedding procession, consisting of a **clergyman, Lucie, Manette,** *and* **Miss Pross** *enters from the other side of the stage. They join Darnay and Lorry. Once the wedding party is in position, the actors freeze.*
Lights build upstage. The mob, led by **Defarge, Mme Defarge,** *the three* **Jacques** *and* **The Vengeance** *pour onto the upstage area. They are armed with improvized weapons such as knives lashed to broomhandles.* **Defarge** *addresses the mob.*

Defarge   Citizens, the day of freedom is here at last! (*Cheers*). Keep near to me, Jacques Three. Jacques Two and Four, separate and put yourselves at the head of as many of these patriots as you can. Where is my wife?

Mme Defarge   Here you see me!

Defarge   Where do you go, my wife?

Mme Defarge   I go with you at present. You shall see me at the head of women, by and by.

Defarge   Come then! Patriots and friends, we are ready. The Bastille!

Mob   The Bastille!

*With a roar, the mob (including **Defarge**, **Mme Defarge**, the three **Jacques** and **The Vengeance**) swarm up the barricade and freeze in a tableau.*
The wedding service becomes briefly audible.

Clergyman ...gathered together in the sight of God to join this man, Charles Darnay, and this woman, Lucie Manette, in ties of holy matrimony, which is an honourable estate....

*The wedding party freezes. The assault on the barricade resumes. The **Citizens** enter and gather downstage opposite to the wedding.*

Citizen 1 Alarm bells ring...

Citizen 2 ...drums beat...

Citizen 3 ...the sea rages and thunders on a new beach.

There is the sound of gunshots and smoke becomes visible. The mob falls back from the barricade.

Citizen 4 Deep ditches...

Citizen 5 ...double drawbridge...

Citizen 6 ...massive stone walls...

Citizen 7 ...eight great towers...

Citizen 8 ...cannon...

Citizen 4 ...muskets...

Citizen 5 ...fire and smoke!

All Citizens Two fierce hours.

*The mob is rallied by **Defarge**.*

Defarge   Work, comrades all, work! Work Jacques Two, Jacques
                     Three...

                                    The mob takes up his cries.

Citizen 3   Jacques One Thousand!

Citizen 2   Jacques Two Thousand!

Citizen 1   Jacques Five-and-Twenty Thousand!

Defarge   In the name of all the angels or the devils – whichever you
                     prefer...work!

Mme Defarge   To me, women!

The Vengeance   What! We can kill as well as the men when the place is taken!

                                    The mob pours forward again. **Defarge**
                                    climbs on top of the barricade.

Defarge   The first drawbridge is down!

                                    The mob cheer, then they freeze.
                                    The wedding service again becomes audible.

Clergyman   Therefore, if any man knows of any just cause or impediment
                     why this woman may not be married to this man, let him speak
                     now, or hereafter, forever hold his peace...

                                    The wedding party freezes.
                                    The struggle at the barricade resumes.
                                    Defenders appear and try to push the mob
                                    back. Hand-to-hand fighting breaks out.

Citizen 4   Deep ditches...

Citizen 5   ...double drawbridge...

Citizen 6   ...massive stone walls...

Citizen 7   ...eight great towers...

Citizen 1	. . . flashing weapons . . .
Citizen 2	. . . blazing torches . . .
Citizen 3	. . . volleys . . .
Citizen 4	. . . curses . . .
Citizen 6	. . . reckless courage . . .
Citizen 7	. . . a roaring sea of living bodies.
All Citizens	Four fierce hours!

The mob freezes. The wedding service resumes.

Clergyman	Do you, Charles Darnay, take Lucie Manette to be your lawful wedded wife? To have and to hold, from this day forward . . .

The wedding party freezes. The action at the barricade resumes. A white flag waves from behind the barricade.

Defarge	Hold! A white flag! They call for a parley!
Citizen 8	See, the last drawbridge is down!
Citizen 5	The prisoners!
Citizen 6	The secret cells!
Citizen 7	The instruments of torture!
Citizen 5	The prisoners!
Defarge	Onwards!

Cheering, the mob swarms over the barricade and off stage.
The wedding service is over. **Darnay** *kisses* **Lucie**.

Manette	May the good Lord grant you joy, my children.
Lorry	My dear Miss Manette. My dear Darnay. I'm quite overcome.
Miss Pross	(*Sniffing*) If only my dear brother Solomon hadn't made a mistake in life . . .

> *Laughing,* **Lucie** *kisses* **Miss Pross***. The wedding party freezes.*
> *The mob (including* **Defarge, Mme Defarge,** *the three* **Jacques** *and* **The Vengeance***) pour on again from the side of the stage pushing a frightened* **jailer** *in front of them.*

Defarge	Show me the North Tower. Quick!
Jailer	Faithfully! . . . but there is no one there.
Defarge	What is the meaning of One Hundred and Five, North Tower? Quick!
Jailer	The meaning, monsieur?
Defarge	Is it a place? A prisoner? For your life!
The Vengeance	Kill him!
Jailer	Monsieur, it is a cell.
Defarge	Show it me!
Mme Defarge	Release the prisoners, my Vengeance.
The Vengeance	And the jailers?
Mme Defarge	Kill them.
The Vengeance	Magnificent!

> *The mob, led by* **The Vengeance** *and the three* **Jacques** *tear off in search of mischief.*

*The **jailer** leads **Defarge** and **Mme**
Defarge off stage. The wedding resumes.
Darnay takes **Manette** aside.*

Darnay   Doctor Manette, when I asked you for your daughter's hand, I
made you a promise. I promised to tell you my true name.

*The wedding party freezes.
The **jailer**, carrying a torch, leads
Defarge and **Mme Defarge** back onto the
stage. They are blindfolded. As they speak,
the **Citizens** handle **Defarge** and **Mme**
Defarge as though playing blind-man's
buff.*

Citizen 2   Through gloomy vaults where light of day has never shone...

Citizen 1   ...past hideous doors of dark dens and cages...

Citizen 3   ...down cavernous flights of steps...

Citizen 4   ...up steep rugged ascents of stone and brick...

Citizen 7   ...while still, the citizens of Saint-Antoine pour into the
fortress like a tide, bent on destruction.

Citizen 6   Winding and climbing up a tower...

Citizen 5   ...hemmed in by massive walls and arches...

Citizen 8   ...until they reach a low, dark door.

Jailer   One Hundred and Five, North Tower.

*The **Citizens** retreat to the shadows and
freeze.
The lights go up on the upstage raised area.
Defarge and **Mme Defarge** tear off their
blindfolds and enter the 'cell'.*

Defarge   (*To jailer*) Pass that torch slowly along these walls, that I may
see them.

*The **jailer** obeys.*

Defarge   Stop! Look here, wife!

Mme Defarge   (*Reading*) 'A. M.'

Defarge   Alexandre Manette. And here he wrote, 'a poor physician'.
                   What more? This stone here?

*Defarge works at a section of the barricade
which opens to reveal a crevice. He
withdraws a small bundle of papers which
he opens and begins to read.
At the same time, the action at the wedding
resumes, becoming simultaneous.*

Darnay   I made a promise to you some little time ago, sir, regarding my
                   name. My mother's name is D'Aulnais. My family name is . . .

Darnay
Defarge   (*Together*) Evrémonde.

Mme Defarge
Manette   (*Together in a whisper*) Evrémonde.

*There is a pause.
Lucie joins **Darnay**. **Manette** raises his
hand in blessing. **Lucie** and **Darnay** exit,
followed by the **clergyman**, **Lorry** and
Miss Pross.
Hustling the **jailer** before them, **Defarge**
and **Mme Defarge** leave the cell and exit.
Manette seems to shrivel as **Darnay** and
Lucie leave the stage. He is suddenly old
and feeble. He retrieves a shoe and
cobblers' tools from the barricade, enters his
'old cell', and begins to hammer.
Miss Pross enters with **Lorry**. **Miss
Pross** gazes in horror at what **Manette** is
doing. **Lorry** approaches Manette slowly
and carefully.*

Lorry	My old friend, will you go out?
Manette	(*Absently*) Out?
Lorry	Yes, for a walk with me? Why not?

> *Manette, as a man asleep, accompanies*
> *Lorry. They walk downstage, followed by*
> *Miss Pross. The lights in the upstage area*
> *dim. The Citizens step forward.*

Citizen 2	Terrors stalk the streets of Paris.
Citizen 6	Vengeance...
Citizen 7	...blood...
Citizen 5	...execution.
Citizen 4	First the sticks...
Citizen 8	...then the stones...
Citizen 3	...then the knives.
Citizen 1	The old jailer falls beneath the feet of the mob.
Citizen 6	Madame Defarge watches him die...
Citizen 7	...and with her cruel knife, long sharpened for the purpose...
Citizen 6	...hacks off his head.
Citizen 1	A rich man, who once told the famished people that they might eat grass, is taken by the mob.
Citizen 3	Madame Defarge has kindly provided him with a rope.
Citizen 2	Once, he is hauled aloft (*The Citizens look up as if watching the hanging*) and the rope breaks, and they catch him shrieking.
Citizen 4	Twice, he is hauled aloft and the rope breaks, and they catch him shrieking.

*Defarge and **Mme Defarge** enter.*

Citizen 7	Then, the rope is merciful and holds him...
Citizen 8	...and soon, his head is on a pike...
Citizen 2	...with grass enough in his mouth for the whole of Saint-Antoine to dance at the sight of.
Defarge	At last, it is come, my dear.
Mme Defarge	Eh, well! Almost.

*Defarge and **Mme Defarge** exit.*
*The **Citizens** freeze.*
*Downstage, **Lorry** has succeeded in*
*bringing **Manette** back to himself.*

Lorry	(*Very gently*) Doctor Manette, I wish to consult you in your professional capacity. You understand?
Manette	You speak...of this attack?
Lorry	I do. What caused it?
Manette	I believe, a strong reminder of the circumstances that first caused the illness.
Lorry	Would the sufferer remember what took place in the relapse?
Manette	Not at all.
Lorry	And, as to the future?
Manette	I believe that a distressing memory has caused a crisis that has now passed. The worst is over. There should be no more attacks.
Lorry	Good. Nevertheless...(*He reaches out for the shoe and tools that Manette still carries*)...would it not be wise, given the nature of the attacks, to remove the occupation the sufferer was used to turn to, during the relapse?

Manette	(*In a trembling voice*) You see, they are such old companions.
Lorry	I am called to our branch in Paris. Terrible things are happening there. I should go with a lighter heart were these things (*Indicating the tools*) destroyed. I would not keep them. For your daughter's sake, Manette.

> **Manette** *nods, and hands over the shoe and tools to* **Lorry,** *who passes them to* **Miss Pross.** **Lorry** *leads* **Manette** *out.* **Miss Pross** *flings the cobblers' gear from her and follows.*
> *Lights down.*

. . . .

Scene 6

> *The* **Citizens** *stand downstage. Flames and smoke appear around and above the barricade.*

Citizen 6	Far away in the country, a château burns...
Citizen 2	...above a village, with a fountain...
Citizen 5	...whose last overlord was murdered...
Citizen 4	...whose successor renounced his title and now lives in England as Mr Charles Darnay.
Citizen 7	Paris burns.
Citizen 3	The court has gone.
Citizen 1	The king with a large jaw...
Citizen 8	...and the queen with a fair face...
Citizen 6	...fly for their lives.
Citizen 1	A new shadow falls over the streets and rooftops of Paris.

*The shadow of an enormous guillotine
appears behind the barricade.*

Citizen 2	On his return home one day, Mr Charles Darnay finds a letter addressed to him...

Enter **Darnay**, *reading.*

Citizen 7	...under that other name...
Citizen 6	...the name he has renounced...
Citizen 8	...which he does not use in England.
Citizen 2	The letter is from his uncle's old servant.

*Defarge, **Mme Defarge**, the three **Jacques** and **The Vengeance** enter, unseen by Darnay. They drive **Gabelle** before them, beating him, and stand watching as **Darnay** paces and **Gabelle** speaks the words of his letter to Darnay.*

Gabelle   'Prison of the Abbaye, Paris. June 21.
'Monsieur heretofore the Marquis, having long been in danger of my life in the village, I have been seized and brought to Paris. My house is burnt. I am accused of treason, Monsieur heretofore the Marquis. They say I have acted for an emigrant. I say that I have acted for, not against the people, according to your commands; that I have collected no rents or taxes; but all is in vain. I shall be summoned before the Tribunal, and shall lose my life. Monsieur heretofore the Marquis, I send my desolate cry across the sea. For the love of Heaven, of justice, of generosity, I beg you to help me, and be true to me as I have been true to you. Your afflicted servant, Gabelle.'

*Miss Pross enters carrying Darnay's coat and bag. **Manette** and **Lucie** enter. **Darnay** takes his leave of them.*

Citizen 1   Charles Darnay takes his leave of his wife and her father.

Citizen 6   Some small matter of business requires him to be from home for a very few days.

Citizen 3   He leaves the house, and takes the Dover mail.

Citizen 8   Charles Darnay sets sail for France.

*Darnay exits. The **Citizens** stand motionless. The only movement is that of **Mme Defarge's** hands, and the only sound that of her needles, as she knits. Blackout.*

. . . .

Act 2

Scene 1

*Paris. The eight **Citizens** are guarding a
barrier to the city. They are armed.
Defarge is amongst them. **Darnay** enters.*

Citizen 1	Charles Darnay...
Citizen 2	...formerly called Evrémonde...
Citizen 3	...travels to Paris.
Citizen 4	On bad roads...
Citizen 5	...in bad carriages...
Citizen 6	...pulled by bad horses.
Citizen 7	But these obstacles are nothing...
Citizen 8	...in these changed times.
Citizen 1	In these changed times, every town gate...
Citizen 2	....and every village taxing house...
All Citizens	...has its band of citizen-patriots.
Citizen 3	In a state of readiness...
Citizens 4 and 5	...a most explosive state of readiness.

Darnay is stopped by the Citizens.

Citizen 3	All travellers are stopped...
Citizen 4	...questioned...
Citizen 5	...cross questioned.
Citizen 3	Have their papers inspected...

Citizen 4	. . . and their names looked for in lists.
Citizen 5	They are turned back . . .
Citizen 6	. . . sent on . . .
Citizen 3	. . . or taken hold of.

Darnay is seized by Citizens 7 and 8.

Citizen 1	All in the name of . . .
Citizen 6	. . . Liberty . . .
Citizen 7	. . . Equality . . .
Citizen 8	. . . Fraternity . . .
All Citizens	. . . or Death!
Defarge	(*To Darnay*) Papers, citizen.

Darnay hands over his papers including the letter from Gabelle. Defarge looks at them then shows them to the gathered Citizens. The Citizens look at them and pass them round. They become more and more agitated.

Citizen 1	He is an emigrant.
Citizen 2	He is an aristocrat.
All Citizens	Down with the emigrant!
Darnay	Emigrant my friends? But I am here in France of my own free will.
Citizen 1	You are a cursed emigrant . . .
Citizen 2	. . . and a cursed aristocrat!

The other Citizens agree.

Citizen 3	Let him be judged!
Citizen 4	Ay . . . and condemned as a traitor!

*The **Citizens** roar their approval. An officer enters.*

Darnay	Friends, I am no traitor!
Citizen 6	He lies.
Citizen 5	He is an emigrant.
Citizen 4	He is a traitor!
Citizen 2	Death to the traitor!
Officer	Silence!

*The noise gradually subsides. A table (with paper, pen and ink) and chair is set up for the **officer** who sits at it. The **officer** calls **Defarge** forward.*

Officer	Citizen Defarge. Is this the emigrant Evrémonde?
Defarge	This is the man.

***Defarge** hands over Darnay's papers.*

Officer	Your age, Evrémonde?
Darnay	Thirty-seven.
Officer	Married, Evrémonde?
Darnay	Yes.
Officer	Where married?
Darnay	In England.
Officer	Without doubt. Where is your wife, Evrémonde?

Darnay	In England.
Officer	Without doubt. You are consigned, Evrémonde, to the prison of La Force.
Darnay	Just Heaven! Under what law and for what offence?
Officer	We have new laws, Evrémonde and new offences since you were here. All emigrants are banished. All those who return are under sentence of death!

*The **Citizens** cheer.*

Darnay	(*Protesting*) But I have come here of my own free will, in response to that written appeal of a fellow countryman that lies before you (*He motions towards Gabelle's letter*) I demand no more than the opportunity to do so without delay. Is that not my right?
Officer	(*Harshly*) Emigrants have no rights, Evrémonde.

*The **officer** writes on a piece of paper and hands it to **Defarge**.*

Officer	In secret!

*The **officer** leaves. The **Citizens** melt into the background. **Defarge** faces **Darnay**.*

Defarge	Is it you, who married the daughter of Doctor Manette who was once a prisoner in the Bastille?
Darnay	(*Surprised*) Yes!
Defarge	My name is Defarge. I keep a wine shop in the quarter of Saint-Antoine. Possibly you have heard of me.
Darnay	My wife came to your house to reclaim her father? Yes!
Defarge	In the name of that sharp female, newly born and called La Guillotine, why did you come to France?
Darnay	You heard me say why a minute ago. It is the truth.

Defarge   It is a bad truth for you.

Darnay   Indeed I am lost here. All here is so changed, so sudden and
                   unfair, that I am absolutely lost. Will you render me a little
                   help?

Defarge   None.

Darnay   (*Pause*) Will you answer me a single question?

Defarge   Perhaps. According to its nature. You can say what it is.

Darnay   In this prison that I am going to so unjustly, shall I have some
                   free communication with the world outside?

Defarge   You will see.

Darnay   I am not to be buried there, prejudged, without any means of
                   presenting my case?

Defarge   You will see. Other people have been buried in worse prisons
                   before now.

Darnay   But never by me, Citizen Defarge.

> *There is a pause as **Defarge** thinks on this.
> A **jailer** enters.*

Darnay   It is of the utmost importance that I should be able to
                   communicate to Mr Lorry of Tellson's Bank in Paris the fact
                   that I have been thrown into the prison of La Force. Will you
                   cause that to be done for me?

Defarge   I will do nothing for you. My duty is to my country and the
                   People. I am the sworn servant of both against you. I will do
                   nothing for you. Jailer! The emigrant Evrémonde!

> ***Defarge** exits. The **jailer** takes charge of
> Darnay. The lights dim. We can barely
> make out shapes of people as they enter and
> wait in the background. There are low
> moans and the sounds of people being
> comforted.*

*A **gentleman** steps forward out of the gloom.*

Gentleman May I have the honour of welcoming you to La Force in the name of your fellow companions in misfortune and misery: The Society of the Dead!

*The lights come up. **Darnay** is confronted by a ragged company of **aristocrats**. They are ghost-like. They present themselves to Darnay, one after the other, curtseying or bowing as appropriate.*
*The **Citizens** introduce them.*

Citizen 1 The ghost of beauty...

Citizen 2 ...the ghost of stateliness...

Citizen 3 ...the ghost of elegance...

Citizen 4 ...the ghost of pride...

Citizen 5 ...the ghost of wit...

Citizen 6 ...the ghost of youth...

Citizen 7 ...the ghost of age.

Gentleman We offer you our sympathy, as we do to all who are so unfortunate as to find themselves in this place. Please forgive my impertinence in asking your name.

Darnay Charles Darnay, formerly called Evrémonde, judged an emigrant.

Gentleman I hope that you are not in secret.

Darnay I do not understand the meaning of the word, but I have heard them say so.

Gentleman Ah what a pity! We so much regret it.

*The **gentleman** turns to the aristocrats.*

Gentleman   I grieve to inform the Society – in secret.

*The **aristocrats** give murmers of
commiseration before melting into the
background. The **Citizens** retreat to the
shadows. The **jailer** places a stool and
bench for Darnay.*

Darnay   Why am I confined alone?

Jailer   How do I know?

Darnay   Can I buy pen, ink, paper?

Jailer   They are not my orders. At present you may buy your food
and nothing more.

*The **jailer** leaves.*

Darnay   Now I am left as if I were dead.

*Darnay begins to pace out the walls of his
cell. The **Citizens**, in the background,
begin to whisper.*

All Citizens   Five paces by four and a half, five paces by four and a half.

Darnay   He made shoes, he made shoes, he made shoes . . .

All Citizens   Five paces by four and a half . . .

*Darnay's pacing and the chanting gets
quicker. He suddenly stands stock still. The
chanting immediately stops. **Darnay's** face
wears an expression of horror.*

Darnay   In secret!

Blackout.

. . . .

Scene 2

*The stage is divided into two. To one side the **Citizens** stand around a grindstone. The other side is a drawing room in Tellson's Bank in Paris. **Lorry** and **Cruncher** are in the room. Lights up on the bank.*

All Citizens   (*A terrifying roar*) Liberty, Equality, Fraternity or Death!

Lorry shivers at the sound.

Lorry   Thank God no one near and dear to us is in this dreadful town. May He have mercy on all the poor souls of Paris who are in danger tonight!

Cruncher   Amen to that, sir. I'd sooner have stayed in Pimlico, myself.

*There is another roar from the **Citizens**. The door bell rings. **Lucie, Carton, Manette** and **Miss Pross** enter.*

Lorry   Lucie! Manette! What is the matter? What has happened to bring you here?

Lucie   (*Embracing Lorry*) Oh my dear friend. It is Charles!

Lorry   What of him?

Carton   He is here.

Lorry   In Paris?

Carton   He has been here some days.

Lucie   He was stopped at the barrier and sent to prison.

> *Lorry looks shocked.*
> *Lights up on the grindstone. There is*
> *another roar from the **Citizens**. They*
> *spring into action around the grindstone,*
> *sharpening their swords, machetes and*
> *knives. They are covered with blood.*

Manette   What is that noise?

Lorry   Don't look out, Manette! For your life don't touch the blind! If they see you...!

Manette   My dear friend, I have a charmed life in this city. I have been a Bastille prisoner. There is no patriot in France who would touch me, except to overwhelm me with embraces or carry me in triumph. This helped us through the barrier and gained us news of Charles. I told you it would be so, my dearest Lucie. I shall help Charles out of all danger.

> *Manette goes over to the Citizens. There is*
> *a tense moment as they move in and a*
> *pause as **Manette** speaks to them.*

Lucie   What are they doing?

Lorry   Don't look! (*He puts his arm round Lucie*) Don't be so terrified, my dear. I swear I know of no harm having happened to Charles, indeed I had no suspicion of him being in this terrible city. What prison is he in?

Lucie   La Force.

Lorry   (*Horrified*) La Force! Lucie, my child, there is no help you can give Charles tonight; you cannot possibly stir out. Leave matters to your father. Rest now. There is nothing you can do. Will you rest?

> *Lucie nods in reluctant agreement and*
> *exits with **Cruncher** and **Miss Pross**.*
> *Lorry and **Carton** watch the Citizens as*
> *Manette pleads his case.*

Lorry	What on earth could have possessed Darnay to come here?
Carton	An errand of generosity; a plea from his old servant. After he had been absent for several days, Mrs Darnay became worried and asked me to find out what had happened to him. I did so. Such investigation is my stock in trade, you may remember.

The Citizens talk among themselves.

Carton	What are those devils about?
Lorry	(*Very quietly*) They are murdering the prisoners! If Doctor Manette has the power that he says, these devils may take him to La Force. It may be too late. I don't know.
Carton	I'll go out and see what news I can find. See no harm comes to Mrs Darnay.

Carton exits. The Citizens cheer. The lights fade on the bank.

Citizen 1	Long live the Bastille prisoner!
All Citizens	Ay!
Citizen 2	Help for the Bastille prisoner's kin in La Force!
All Citizens	Save the prisoner Evrémonde!

Citizens 1, 2, 3, and 4 lead Manette off.

Citizen 5	The next four nights are nights of blood.
Citizen 6	Eleven hundred prisoners killed...
Citizen 7	...in the name of Liberty, Equality, Fraternity...
Citizens 5–8	...and Death!
Citizen 8	For four nights, the doctor does not return.
Citizen 5	For four long nights there is no news.

Citizen 6   Four long nights of waiting.

Citizen 7   Four nights of vengeance!

Citizen 8   Four long nights of wondering.

Citizen 6   Four nights of death!

Citizen 5   Four long nights of hoping.

Citizen 7   Four nights of slaughter!

Citizen 5   Four long nights of praying.

Citizen 8   Four nights of blood!

> *The **Citizens** roar their approval.
> Lights down on the grindstone and back up
> on Tellson's Bank where **Lorry** sits waiting
> for news. **Cruncher** enters.*

Cruncher   Visitors sir. They say they have news of Doctor Manette.

Lorry   Thank God! By Heaven I hope it is good. Show them in, quickly.

> *Defarge, Mme Defarge and The
> Vengeance enter. Mme Defarge is
> knitting.*

Lorry   (*Standing*) Your servant.

> *He looks carefully at Defarge.*

Lorry   Do you know me?

Defarge   Do you know *me*?

Lorry   I have seen you somewhere.

Defarge   Perhaps at my wine shop?

Lorry   Yes. And your wife? Madame Defarge, surely? And . . . ?

> *He indicates The Vengeance.* **Mme**
> **Defarge** *continues knitting.*

Defarge Madame's companion is known as The Vengeance.

Lorry Ah yes. (*To Defarge*) You come from Doctor Manette?

Defarge Yes. He sends this to you.

> ***Defarge** hands **Lorry** a note.*

Lorry (*Reading*) 'Charles is safe, but I cannot safely leave this place yet. I have obtained the favour that the bearer has a short note from Charles to his wife. Let the bearer see Lucie.' (*Calling out*) Lucie! Lucie!

> *Lucie enters.*

Lorry Charles is safe! These people have brought news! They have a note from Charles.

> ***Lucie** is overwhelmed. She takes the offered note.*

Lucie (*Reading*) 'Dearest, take courage. I am well, and your father has influence.' Oh thank you!

> ***Lucie** drops to her knees, takes **Mme**
> **Defarge**'s hand and kisses it. **Mme**
> **Defarge** does not stop knitting. **Lucie** looks
> up to meet the hard stare of **Mme**
> **Defarge**.*

Mme Defarge It is enough, my husband. I have seen her. We may go.

Lucie You will be good to my poor husband? You will help me to see him if you can?

Mme Defarge Your husband is not my business. What does he say in that letter? Something about influence?

Lucie That my father has much influence.

Mme Defarge	Surely it will release him.
The Vengeance	Let it do so. (*She cackles with laughter*)
Lucie	I implore you to have pity on me and not to exercise any power you have against my innocent husband. For my sake as a wife and a fellow sister.
Mme Defarge	The wives and fellow sisters we have known have not been greatly considered. We have known their husbands and fathers laid in prisons and kept there. All our lives we have seen our sister-women suffer in themselves and in their children, poverty, hunger, nakedness, thirst, sickness, misery, oppression and neglect. Is it likely that the trouble of one wife would mean much to us now?

*There is a pause before **The Vengeance**, **Mme Defarge** and **Defarge** leave.*

Lorry	Courage, Lucie. So far it all goes well with us. Cheer up and have a thankful heart.
Lucie	I am not thankless I hope, but that dreadful woman seems to throw a shadow on me and on all my hopes.
Lorry	Tut, what is this despondancy? A shadow indeed. There's no substance in it, Lucie. Your father will gain Charles' liberty.

*The lights go down on Tellson's Bank and up on the **Citizens** who are grouped downstage.*
The shadow of the guillotine is visible behind the barricade.

Citizen 1	But though the doctor tries hard to have Darnay released...
Citizen 2	...Charles Darnay remains in La Force.
Citizen 1	And meanwhile, the new era has begun...
Citizen 7	...as three hundred thousand men...
Citizen 8	...summoned to rise against the tyrants of the earth...

Citizen 7	. . . rise from the soils of France.
Citizen 8	There is no pause . . .
Citizen 1	. . . no pity . . .
Citizen 2	. . . no peace.
Citizen 3	Terror and Madame La Guillotine rule the land.
Citizen 4	La Guillotine . . .
Citizen 5	. . . the best cure for headaches!
Citizen 4	La Guillotine . . .
Citizen 6	. . . the National Razor that shaves too close!
Citizen 4	La Guillotine . . .
Citizen 7	. . . barber to the sacred head of the King, and the grey hair of the Queen.
Citizen 4	La Guillotine . . .
Citizen 8	. . . our new religion!
Citizen 1	Every day, through the streets, the tumbrils roll, filled with the condemned.
Citizen 2	Lovely girls, bright women . . .
Citizen 3	. . . brown-haired, black-haired and grey.
Citizen 4	Youths, stalwart men and old.
Citizen 5	Gentle born and peasant born.
Citizen 6	All red wine for Madame Guillotine.
All Citizens	Amen!
Citizens 1–4	Charles Darnay is summoned!

| Citizens 5–8 | He is to stand before the Tribunal . . . tomorrow. |

Blackout.

. . . .

Scene 3

*The Tribunal. The **President** sits at a bench on which there is a bell. **Citizen 3** takes the role of the prosecutor. **Defarge, Mme Defarge, The Vengeance, Jacques 2, 3** and **4, Lucie, Manette, Lorry, Miss Pross** and **Cruncher** are present. **Gabelle** is also there, as is **Carton**, unnoticed. **Darnay** stands in the dock. The remaining **Citizens** act as jury and the court is crowded with spectators.*

Citizen 3	Charles Evrémonde, called Darnay. You are accused of being an emigrant and as such your life is forfeit to the Republic. All emigrants are under sentence. You returned and were taken. Therefore the Republic demands your head!
Citizen 1	Death to the traitor!
Spectators	Liberty, Fraternity, Equality and Death!

*The **President** rings a bell. The cries are quietened.*

President	Evrémonde, is it true that you have lived for many years in England?
Darnay	It is.
President	Therefore is it not true that you are an emigrant?
Darnay	Not in the spirit of the law. I gave up both a title and a station that was distasteful to me. It is true that I left this country and, as you rule, that is the definition of an emigrant. But I left France in order to live by my own industry rather than on the industry of the overladen people of France.

The spectators murmer their approval.

President   But you have married in England.

Darnay   It is true, but not an English woman. A French citizen by birth. Lucie Manette, the only daughter of Doctor Manette, the good physican who sits there.

Darnay motions to Manette. The spectators cheer.

President   Why did you return to France when you did?

Darnay   I returned in response to a letter written by a French citizen who claimed that his life was in danger because of my absence. I returned to tell the truth and so save his life despite any personal danger to me. Is this a criminal act in the eyes of the Republic?

Spectators   No!

The President rings the bell. The cries subside.

President   Where is this person? Can he confirm this?

Gabelle steps forward.

Gabelle   Citizen President, I am Citizen Gabelle. I did indeed write such a letter to Citizen Evrémonde. And indeed, it is because he has been taken that I have been released through the mercy of the Tribunal.

The spectators cry in support of Darnay. The President rings the bell once more.

President   Is there any one else who can answer for the prisoner Evrémonde?

Citizen 5   The Bastille prisoner!

Citizen 6   The good doctor!

Citizen 7	Citizen Manette!

*The **Citizens** repeat these calls for Manette. He comes forward.*

Manette   As you know, I myself was imprisoned in the Bastille for many years . . .

The spectators call out 'shame' etc.

Manette   . . . it was this man who first befriended me on my release. During my exile in England, he has remained faithful to both me and my daughter. He is now my kin. It has been suggested that he is in league with the English aristocratic government. This is a lie. Indeed, they too have tried him as a foe and a traitor. This can be confirmed by an English gentleman who is present today, Mr Jarvis Lorry.

Lorry   (*Calling out*) It is true, 'pon my life!

Manette   As a friend of the Republic and a former prisoner of the Bastille, I beg you to release this man.

Citizen 1   (*To the President*) We are ready to deliver our verdict, Citizen President.

President   How do you find the prisoner?

All Citizens   Not guilty!

*There is a roar of approval. **Manette**, **Lucie**, **Lorry** and **Darnay** are very relieved. **Mme Defarge** looks furious and whispers something to her husband and **The Vengeance**. **Defarge** seems to argue, but moves to confer with the three **Jacques**. **Lucie** and **Darnay** embrace. **Carton** looks on unnoticed in the background.*
*The **President** exits. The court begins to clear. **Defarge**, **Mme Defarge** and **The Vengeance** exit. The **Citizens** move downstage.*

Darnay	Lucie, I am safe!
Lucie	Dearest Charles, thank God!
Manette	Miss Pross, find food and drink. We are able to celebrate! Jerry accompany Miss Pross. Keep her safe!
Lorry	I shall prepare the rooms to receive us!

Miss Pross, Cruncher and Lorry leave.

Citizen 4	No garret.
Citizen 5	No shoemaking.
Citizen 6	No One Hundred and Five, North Tower.
Citizen 7	No guillotine.
Citizen 8	His promise is redeemed.
Manette	I have saved him!

*But at this moment of triumph **Jacques 2, 3** and **4** step forward.*

Jacques 2	The citizen Evrémonde, called Darnay?
Darnay	Who seeks him?
Jacques 4	We seek him. I know you Evrémonde.
Jacques 3	You are again the prisoner of the Republic.

*There are shocked reactions from **Manette, Lucie** and **Darnay**.*

Darnay	Tell me why am I again a prisoner?
Jacques 2	It is enough for you to know that you will go straight to the prison of the Conciergerie.

Carton leaves unnoticed.

Jacques 3	You are summoned for tomorrow.

Manette moves to the Jacques.

Manette	Do you know me?
Jacques 4	We all know you.
Manette	Answer me then. Why does this happen?
Jacques 2	Citizen Doctor, he has been denounced by the section of Saint-Antoine. (*Indicating Jacques 3*) This citizen is from Saint-Antoine.
Jacques 3	He is accused by Saint-Antoine.
Manette	Of what?
Jacques 4	Citizen Doctor, ask no more. If the Republic makes demands from you, without doubt you as a good patriot will be happy to answer them. The Republic goes before all. The People is supreme.
Jacques 2	Come, Evrémonde.

The three Jacques move to take Darnay away.

Manette	(*Desperately*) Will you tell me who denounced him?
Jacques 3	He is gravely denounced by the Citizen and Citizeness Defarge. And by one other.
Manette	What other?
Jacques 3	Do *you* ask, doctor?
Manette	Yes . . . who?
Jacques 3	Then you will be answered tomorrow. Now I am dumb!

Darnay is led away, Manette is left comforting Lucie. Blackout.

Scene 4

The Defarges' wine shop. **Mme Defarge** *is standing behind the bar. At a table,* **Defarge** *consults the three* **Jacques**. *The* **Citizens** *are drinking quietly around the shop.* **Barsad** *is among them.* **Carton** *is also present but keeps his face hidden until he speaks. Enter* **Miss Pross** *and* **Cruncher**.

Miss Pross	Wine for my ladybird! Now he is away from that dreadful place.
Cruncher	A celebration! Just like old times, Mr Darnay being freed and at liberty.
Miss Pross	Don't talk about liberty, we've had quite enough of that talk in this country!
Cruncher	Please miss, hush, remembrin' where we is!

> ***Cruncher** guides **Miss Pross** through the Citizens towards the bar.*

Miss Pross	Look at these creatures. They have but one meaning, and it's midnight murder and mischief.
Cruncher	Hush! Please be cautious miss.
Miss Pross	Yes, I'll be cautious, but remember, Mr Cruncher that the short and the long of it, is that I am a subject of His Most Gracious Majesty King George the Third...

> ***Miss Pross** curtseys. The **Citizens** look threatening. **Cruncher** is worried.*

Miss Pross	...and what I say is, 'Confound their politics, Frustrate their knavish tricks, On him our hopes we fix, God save the...'
Cruncher	(*Stopping her*) Sshhhhh! Beggin' your pardon miss, but remember where we is!

> *Cruncher moves **Miss Pross** forward to the bar, smiling at the Citizens, apologizing with signs (as he speaks no French) for the behaviour of a 'senseless old woman'.*
> ***Barsad** gets up from a group and pushes in front of **Miss Pross** and **Cruncher**. **Miss Pross** stares at him, **Barsad** stares back. **Miss Pross** lets out a scream. The occupants of the bar jump up. **Miss Pross** and **Barsad** stare at each other. **Cruncher** stares as though he has seen a ghost. When the **Citizens** realize it is not anything as interesting as a squabble or a fight, they sit down and resume their chatter.*

Miss Pross	Solomon, dear Solomon. After not setting eyes on you for so long, I find you here in all places!
Barsad	Don't call me Solomon. Do you want to be the death of me?
Miss Pross	Brother, brother! How can you ask me such a cruel question?
Barsad	Then hold your tongue. Who is this man?
Miss Pross	Mr Cruncher.
Barsad	Why does he stare so? Does he think me a ghost?

> ***Barsad** pulls **Miss Pross** and **Cruncher** to a table away from the rest.*

Barsad	Now what do you want?
Miss Pross	How unkind for a brother to give me such a greeting and show me no affection.

Barsad sighs, leans forward and pecks
Miss Pross *on the cheek.*

Barsad   There. Now are you content?

Miss Pross shakes her head and begins to weep.

Barsad   If you expect me to be surprised, I am not. I knew you were here; I know of most people who are here. If you really do not wish to endanger my existence then go your way as soon as possible and let me go mine. I am busy, I am an official.

Miss Pross   My brother Solomon, that had the makings of one of the best and greatest of men in his native country, an official amongst foreigners, and such foreigners!

Barsad looks around, and tries to quieten Miss Pross.

Barsad   (*Whispering harshly*) I said so! I knew it. You will be the death of me. Just as I am getting on!

Cruncher   Beggin' pardon, sir, but might I ask a question as to whether your name is John Solomon or Solomon John?

Barsad   What?

Cruncher   Come! Speak out! John Solomon or Solomon John? She calls you Solomon and she must know being your sister. And *I* know you're John. Which of the two goes first? And regarding the name of Pross; well that warn't your name over the water.

Barsad   What do you mean?

Cruncher   Well I don't know all I mean, for I can't call to mind what your name was, over the water. But I'll swear it was a name of two syllables.

Barsad   Indeed?

Cruncher   Yes. I know you. You was a spy-witness at the Bailey. What in the name of the father of lies, was you called at that time?

Carton steps forward to the table.

Carton	Barsad.
Cruncher	That's the name!
Carton	My dear Miss Pross; Mr Cruncher; I have to pass on bad news. Mr Darnay has been arrested again.
Miss Pross	What do you say! We left him safe and free within these two hours!
Carton	Arrested for all that. Now I wish to beg a little talk with your brother. I wish that you had a better employed brother than Mr Barsad. I wish for your sake that he was not a spy of the prisons.
Barsad	(*Looking around worried*) How dare you sir ...
Carton	I'll tell you how I dare, sir. I have made enquiries. I have found out things. It is my business to find out things. I saw you coming out of the prison of the Conciergerie. You have a face to remember and I remember faces well. Made curious by seeing you in that connection and associating you with the misfortunes of Mr Darnay, I followed you to this wine shop and sat close to you. From your talk, I had no difficulty in deducing the nature of your work. Gradually, from what seemed to have happened at chance, a purpose has come into my mind.
Barsad	What purpose?
Carton	All in good time. Mr Cruncher, would you be willing to escort Miss Pross back to her lodgings, whilst I make her brother a proposition?
Cruncher	Certainly sir.
Barsad	(*To Miss Pross*) I told you so, if any trouble comes of this, it's your doing.

Carton	Come, come, Mr Barsad. Don't be ungrateful. But for my great respect for your sister, I might not have led so pleasantly to a little proposal that I wish to make for our mutual satisfaction. Miss Pross, Mr Cruncher, good day to you.

> *Miss Pross goes to wish Barsad farewell; he grudgingly accepts it.* **Cruncher** *and* **Miss Pross** *leave.* **Carton** *sits with Barsad at the table, with a bottle of brandy. He pulls a deck of cards from his pocket and plays with them, seemingly absent-mindedly, whilst talking to Barsad.*

Carton	Now Mr Barsad, I trust that the name and the influence of Doctor Manette will stand Mr Darnay in good stead when he is taken before the Tribunal. But it may not be so. I admit to you that I am shaken by the doctor not having the power to prevent the arrest. In short, Mr Barsad, this is a desperate time, when desperate games are played for desperate stakes. Now, the stake I have resolved to play for in case of the worst, is a friend in the Conciergerie. And the friend I purpose to win is you, Mr Barsad.
Barsad	You need to have good cards, sir.
Carton	I'll run them over. I'll see what I hold.

> *Carton takes a sip of brandy and arranges the cards in his hand, before taking one and looking at it.*

Carton	Mr Barsad, the spy of the prisons, informer to the Republican committees, has presented himself to his employers under a false name. (*Carton places the card down before Barsad*) That's a very good card. (*He takes another card and holds it before him*) Mr Barsad, now in the employ of the Republican French government, was formerly in the employ of the aristocratic English government, the enemy of France and freedom. (*He places this card down*) That's an excellent card. (*He takes another card*) It suggests that Mr Barsad is still spying for England and a treacherous foe of the Republic. (*He places this card down too*) That's a card not to be beaten. Have you followed my hand, Mr Barsad?

Barsad	I do not understand your play.
Carton	(*Taking an ace from the deck*) I play my ace. An accusation that Mr Barsad is a spy and traitor is made to the nearest citizens' committee. (*He indicates the Citizens*) Look over your hand, Mr Barsad and see what you have. Don't hurry. (*He calls to Mme Defarge*) A glass of wine, citizen if you please!

> *Mme Defarge casts a glance at Carton, then looks more intensely at him.* **Barsad** *cringes.*

Mme Defarge	What did you say, citizen?
Carton	A glass of wine.
Mme Defarge	You are English?
Carton	Yes, madame, I am English.

> *Mme Defarge takes Carton a glass of wine. He toasts her and the Republic. She returns to Defarge.*

Mme Defarge	I swear to you, he looks like Evrémonde!
Defarge	Certainly a little like.
Mme Defarge	I tell you a good deal like!
Barsad	(*To Carton*) For God's sake don't draw attention to yourself. Do you *want* to be noticed in this place?
Carton	Oh, yes. It is necessary.
Barsad	I don't.

> *Barsad shivers. Many customers whisper, gazing at Carton. The name 'Evrémonde' can be heard among the whispering.*

Carton	You scarcely seem to like your hand. Do you play?

Barsad	I appeal to you, sir, whether you will take it upon yourself to play your ace. I admit I am a spy, but surely you would not sink so low as to play the spy yourself?
Carton	I play my ace, Mr Barsad, without any scruple, in a very few minutes.
Barsad	I should have hoped that your respect for my sister would...
Carton	I could not better testify my respect for your sister than by finally relieving her of her brother.
Barsad	(*Bitterly*) You think not sir?
Carton	I have thoroughly made up my mind about it.
Barsad	You told me you had a proposal. What is it? It is no use asking too much of me. What do you want?
Carton	Not very much. You are a jailer at the Conciergerie?
Barsad	I tell you once and for all, there is no such thing as an escape possible.
Carton	Why need you tell me what I have not asked? You are a turnkey at the Conciergerie?
Barsad	I am sometimes.
Carton	You can be when you choose.
Barsad	I can pass in and out when I choose.

Carton picks up the bottle, empties the brandy into his glass and tips the glass so that the brandy spills onto the table. He leans towards Barsad.

Carton	Let us have one final word. This is what I propose...

Lights fade to blackout.

. . . .

Scene 5

The lights go up to reveal the Tribunal. The court is again crowded with spectators. The Citizens are present as the jury. Defarge and Mme Defarge are present with The Vengeance and the Jacques. Manette sits with Lucie, Lorry, Miss Pross and Cruncher. Carton is in the background. Citizen 3 is once again the prosecutor. Darnay is accompanied by a jailer. The President of the Tribunal enters and sits at his bench.

Citizen 3   Charles Evrémonde, called Darnay. Released yesterday, re-accused and retaken yesterday. The charge was delivered last night. He is a suspected and denounced enemy of the Republic, one of a family of aristocrats, who used their abolished privileges to oppress the people. By the law of the Republic, Evrémonde's life is forfeit to the People.

The spectators cheer at this.

President   Is the accused denounced openly or secretly?

Citizen 3   Openly, Citizen President.

President   By whom?

Citizen 3   Three voices. Ernest Defarge, wine vendor of Saint-Antoine.

President   Good.

Citizen 3   Thérèse Defarge, his wife.

President   Good.

Citizen 3   Alexandre Manette, physician!

There is uproar in the court. Manette jumps up, the Citizens and spectators bellow, the President rings his bell to restore order.

Manette	President, I protest to you that this is a forgery and a fraud. You know the accused to be the husband of my daughter. My daughter and those dear to her are far dearer to me than my life. Who and where is the false conspirator who says that I denounce the husband of my child!
President	Citizen Manette, be tranquil. To fail in submission to the authority of the Tribunal would be to put yourself out of law. As to what is dearer to you than life, nothing can be so dear to a good citizen as the Republic.

*The spectators and the **Citizens** cheer this loudly.*

President	If the Republic should demand of you the sacrifice of your child herself, you would have no duty but to sacrifice her. Listen to what is to follow. In the meantime, be quiet!

*There is more cheering. **Defarge** steps forward.*

Citizen 3	Citizen Defarge, you were a former servant of the citizen doctor.
Defarge	I was.
Citizen 3	And when he was released from his time in the Bastille, you took care of him.
Defarge	I did.
Citizen 3	You did good service at the taking of the Bastille?
Defarge	I believe so.
The Vengeance	You were one of the best patriots there!

*The spectators and the **Citizens** roar their approval.*

Citizen 3	You were among the first to enter that place?

The Vengeance   He was! Citizens, I speak the truth!

*The spectators and the **Citizens** cheer again. The **President** rings the bell to restore order.*

Citizen 3   Inform the Tribunal of what you did the day within the Bastille, citizen.

Defarge   I knew that this prisoner of whom I speak had been confined in a cell known as One Hundred and Five, North Tower. I knew it from himself. He knew himself by no other name than One Hundred and Five, North Tower. On the day the Bastille fell, I resolved to examine that cell. I found it and examined it very closely. In a hole in the chimney, I discovered a stone had been worked out and there I found a written paper. This is it. (*He brandishes an old worn document*) It is written in the handwriting of Doctor Manette. I confide this paper to the hands of the President.

Defarge hands the document to the President.

President   Let it be read out.

*The **President** gives **Manette** the document. **Manette** then moves to the raised upstage area. This is set with a table and chair. The lights dim and the jury and court fade into the background. Isolated in a spotlight, **Manette** sits in his cell in the Bastille.*

Manette   I, Alexandre Manette, unfortunate physician, native of Beauvais, write this paper in the Bastille, during the last month of the year 1767. I write it at stolen intervals and secrete it in the wall of the chimney. Some pitying hand may find it there when I and my troubles are dust. I write these words with a rusty iron point, charcoal, soot and blood in the tenth year of my captivity. Hope has departed from my breast, but I solemnly declare that I am in the possession of my right mind – my memory is exact. Whether this paper is ever found or not, I will swear that what I write is the truth before the throne of God Himself.

Manette gets up and moves downstage. The light changes to moonlight in the downstage area. In the other downstage area, in darkness, a carriage is created as for previous scenes.

Manette   One cloudy moonlit night in the third week of December in 1757, I was walking...

The Citizens step forward and surround Manette.

Citizen 4   ...on a frosty night...

Citizen 5   ...by the side of the River Seine...

Citizen 6   ...when a carriage...

Citizen 7   ...driven at speed...

Citizen 8   ...comes alongside...

Citizen 4   ...and hurtles past.

Citizen 5   A head appears at the window.

Citizen 6   A voice calls out...

All Citizens   ...STOP!

Citizen 6   Two gentlemen...

Citizen 7   ...wrapped in cloaks...

Citizen 8   ...step out.

The two gentlemen enter. They are the Marquis and his brother but their identities are concealed by their cloaks.

Marquis   You are Doctor Manette?

Manette   I am.

Brother   Doctor Manette, the young physician, originally an expert surgeon, who within the last year or two has made a rising reputation?

Manette   Gentlemen, I am that doctor of whom you speak so graciously.

Marquis   Will you please enter the carriage?

> *The **Marquis** and his **brother** move forward to surround Manette. The **Citizens** look concerned.*

All Citizens   Armed!

> *The **Marquis** brandishes a pistol.*

Manette   Gentlemen, pardon me but I usually enquire who does me the honour to seek my assistance, and what is the nature of the case to which I am summoned.

Brother   Doctor, your clients are gentlemen. As to the nature of the case, it is your business to discover it rather than ours to describe it. Enough. Will you please enter the carriage?

> *The lights come up on the carriage.*

Citizen 4   The doctor has no choice; he enters the carriage.

> *Manette, the **Marquis** and his **brother** sit in the carriage. The sounds of the carriage starting up are heard.*

Citizen 5   It drives away...

Citizen 6   ...leaving the streets behind.

Citizen 7   Past the north barrier and into the country.

Citizen 8   Two thirds of a league past the barrier...

Citizen 4   ...it stops at a solitary house.

There are sounds of the carriage pulling up. **Manette,** *the* **Marquis** *and his* **brother** *get out and cross to the other downstage area; the* **Citizens** *follow. The lights go down on the carriage.*

Citizen 5   They enter the house...

Citizen 6   ...the gentlemen remove their cloaks.

Citizen 7   Exactly alike! They cannot be told apart!

Citizen 8   Twins!

Marquis   Come with us.

The lights reveal a **woman** *lying on a bed. The* **Marquis,** *his* **brother** *and* **Manette** *go to her, followed by* **Citizens 1, 2, 3** *and* **4.**

Citizen 1   A woman of great beauty...

Citizen 4   ...and young...

Citizen 3   ...not much past twenty.

Citizen 1   Hair torn and ragged...

Citizen 2   ...her arms bound to her sides with sashes and a handkerchief.

Manette   I saw all this. My first act was to put out my hands to her. I saw on the handkerchief the sign of a noble and the letter E.

Woman   (*Shrieking*) My husband, my father and my brother. One, two, three, four, five, six, seven, eight, nine, ten, eleven, twelve...Hush! My husband, my father and my brother.

Citizen 4   She counts to twelve again.

                                        The ***woman*** *counts to twelve under her breath.*

Woman   Hush!

Citizen 3   A pause...

Woman   My husband, my father and my brother...

                                        The ***woman*** *resumes the count to twelve under her breath during the following dialogue.*

Manette   How long has this lasted?

Marquis   Since about this hour last night.

Manette   Has she a husband, a father, and a brother?

Marquis   A brother.

Manette   Are you her brother?

Marquis   (*With contempt*) No.

Manette   Has she some recent association with the number twelve?

Brother   With twelve o'clock!

Manette   Gentlemen, if I had known what I was coming to see, I could have brought medicines with me. As it is, there are none to be obtained in this lonely place.

Brother   There is a case of medicines here.

*The **Marquis' brother** takes a case from the barricade. **Manette** opens some of the bottles in the case and smells them.*

Brother   Do you doubt them?

Manette   You see, monsieur, I am going to use them.

*Manette feeds some of the medicine to the **woman**. She continues her cries. They gradually quieten.*

Marquis   There is another patient.

Manette   (*Startled*) Another! Is it a pressing case?

Marquis   You had better see.

*Manette, the Marquis and his **brother** move across stage, followed by **Citizens 5, 6, 7** and **8**. The **woman** and **Citizens 1** to **4** freeze. The lights reveal that the carriage has been replaced by a bed of straw. A **boy** lies on it. He clutches his chest with his hand. The four **Citizens** inspect him.*

Citizen 8   Another patient...

Citizen 5   ...in the stable loft.

Citizen 6   A peasant boy...

Citizen 7   ...not yet seventeen and handsome.

Manette kneels over him.

Manette   I am a doctor, my poor fellow. Let me examine it.

Boy   I do not want it examined. Let it be.

Manette prises the boy's hand away from his chest.

Citizens 5–8	(*Shocked*) A sword wound!
Citizen 5	No doctor will save him. He is dying.
Manette	How has this been done?
Marquis	He is a crazed young common dog! A serf! He forced my brother to draw upon him, and has fallen by my brother's sword – like a gentleman!
Boy	Doctor, they are proud, these nobles; but we common dogs are proud too, sometimes. They plunder us, outrage us, beat us, kill us; but we have a little pride left sometimes. Have you seen her, doctor?
Manette	I have.
Boy	She is my sister, doctor. They have had their shameful rights, these nobles, with the virtue and modesty of our sisters, but we have good girls among us. My sister was a good girl. She was betrothed to a good young man. We were all tenants of his. (*He points at the Marquis*) That man who stands there. The other is his brother – the worst of a bad race. We were robbed by that man there as are all common dogs by those 'superior beings'!
Citizen 7	Taxed by him without mercy . . .
Citizen 5	. . . obliged to work for him without pay . . .
Citizen 6	. . . obliged to grind our corn at his mills.
Citizen 7	Pillaged and plundered . . .
Citizen 8	. . . robbed and hunted.
Citizen 6	And made so poor, that our fathers tell us that it is a terrible thing to bring children into the world!
Citizen 5	The boy clings to life to tell his story.
Citizen 6	The story of how his sister married her lover.
Citizen 7	So that she might comfort him.

Citizen 8   Of how she was seen by the brother of the Marquis...

Citizen 7   ...who admired her...

Citizen 5   ...and wanted her. It was the man's right.

Citizen 6   The right of the the noble race...

Citizen 7   ...the right of superior beings.

Citizen 8   But she refused.

Boy   She is a good girl.

> *Citizens 5, 6, 7 and 8 turn to the boy before continuing the story.*

Citizen 8   So they put her husband to work.

Citizen 5   Every hour...

Citizen 6   ...of every day...

Citizen 7   ...of every night.

Citizen 8   It is their right.

Citizen 6   Until one day at noon, he sobs twelve times and dies in her arms.

Citizens 5–8   One, two, three, four, five, six, seven, eight, nine, ten, eleven, twelve. Hush!

Boy   Then they took my sister away for his pleasure. The shock of it killed our father. So I tracked this noble man down, but not before I had hidden my younger sister far away, so that they will never find her. Last night I came here. He tried to bribe me with money, then he struck at me, first with a whip then his sword. And so I lie. Lift me up, doctor. Turn my face to him.

*Manette adjusts the **boy** to face the*
***Marquis** and his **brother**. The **boy** raises*
his hand.

Boy   Marquis, in the days when all these things are to be answered
for, I summon you and yours to the last of your bad race to
answer for them. I mark this cross of blood upon you as a sign
that I do it.

*The **boy** puts his hand to his chest, covers*
it with blood and makes a sign of the cross
with his forefinger. As he drops his hand he
*dies. There is a pause as **Manette** lies him*
down. Lights down on the boy.

Marquis   The woman...?

*Manette, the **Marquis** and his **brother***
cross to the other side of the stage, followed
*by **Citizens** 5, 6, 7 and 8. The **woman***
*still lies there surrounded by **Citizens** 1, 2,*
3 and 4.

Marquis   Is she dead?

Manette   Not yet, but like to die.

Brother   What strength there is in these common bodies.

Manette   There is great strength in sorrow and despair.

Marquis   Take her away!

*Citizens 7 and 8 remove the **woman**.*

Marquis   Doctor, your reputation is high and as a young man with your
fortune to make, you know what is best for your interests. (*He
looks at his brother before turning back to Manette*) The things
that you see here are things to be seen and not spoken of...

*The **Marquis** and his **brother** stare at*
Manette. He has understood their threats.

Brother	(*Handing **Manette** a bag of coins*) Doctor, for your troubles.
Manette	Pray, excuse me. Under the circumstances, no.

> *The **Marquis** and his **brother** stare again at Manette, then turn sharply and step back into the shadows.*

Manette	I returned home, greatly troubled and resolved to write privately to the Minister, stating what I had seen and heard. I knew what court influence was, and what immunities the aristocracy had, and I expected that I would hear nothing more of the matter. I told no one else of what had happened, not even my wife as I feared what might happen to any one who shared this knowledge. That night after delivering my letter to the Minister, I had another visitor.

> *Citizen 2 takes the part of the visitor and steps forward.*

Citizen 2	Doctor, there is an urgent case in the Rue St Honore. It is most important that you attend the patient. I have a coach waiting . . .

> *Manette steps forward. He is suddenly grabbed by **Citizens** 3 and 4. The **Marquis** and his **brother** step forward.*

Marquis	This is the man.
Brother	And this is his letter!

> *He waves Manette's letter in his face before ripping it up.*

Marquis	(*Motioning to the Citizens*) The Bastille!

> *The **Marquis** and his **brother** exit. The **Citizens** take Manette upstage then they melt into the shadows. **Manette** is now back in his cell.*

Manette   By the act of these brothers, I was imprisoned, without trial and in secret. If they had allowed me some news of my wife in all those years of torment, I might have believed there was some good in them. Now I believe that the mark of the red cross is fatal to them. All their crimes will be answered for. I, Alexandre Manette, unhappy prisoner of the Bastille, do this last night of the year 1767, in unbearable agony, denounce to Heaven and earth both them and their decendants to the very last of their race. I denounce the family of Evrémonde.

Blackout.
***Citizens** 7 and 8 enter. The lights come up to reveal the Tribunal and **Manette** who remains seated in his cell, his head bowed in his hands. There is uproar from the **Citizens** and the spectators.*

Spectators   Death to the aristocrat!

Citizen 1   Guilty!

Citizen 2   An aristocrat!

Citizen 4   An enemy of the Republic!

Mme Defarge   Much influence he has, that doctor. Save him now, doctor, save him!

President   Death within twenty-four hours!

*The **Citizens** and spectators roar their approval. The **jailer** and two **Citizens** move to take Darnay away. The rest of the court clears leaving **Lucie, Darnay, Manette, Lorry, Cruncher, Miss Pross, Carton,** two **Citizens** and the **jailer** on stage.*
***Lucie** moves forward towards Darnay.*

Lucie   If I might embrace him! O, good citizens, if you would have so much compassion for us!

Jailer   Let them embrace; it is but a moment.

Lucie and Darnay embrace.

Darnay
Farewell, dear darling of the soul. My parting blessing on my love. We shall meet again when the weary are at rest.

Lucie
I can bear it dear Charles, I am supported by above. We shall not be separated long.

Manette comes forward from his cell and goes to kneel before Darnay and Lucie.

Darnay
No! Do not kneel. I know now how great a sacrifice you made when you allowed me to marry Lucie. We know now what you underwent when you realized my family name, and that the wrongs you suffered were brought upon you by my father and uncle. I know the feelings you fought and conquered for Lucie's sake. We thank you with all our hearts, and our love and duty. Heaven be with you!

Manette shakes his head miserably.

Darnay
It could not be otherwise. Good could never come of such evil. Be comforted and forgive me. Heaven bless you.

Darnay is led away. Lucie collapses and is caught by Carton. She is surrounded by Lorry, Manette, Miss Pross and Cruncher.

Carton
I have her. I shall not let her fall.

Carton picks Lucie up and gazes fondly at her for a moment.

Carton
(*Whispering*) A life you love... She should be taken home. Cruncher, Miss Pross...

Cruncher takes Lucie from Carton. Cruncher and Miss Pross leave with Lucie.

Carton	You had great influence yesterday, Doctor Manette. These judges and all the men in power are friendly to you, are they not? Try them again. The hours between this and tomorrow are few and short.
Manette	I intend to try.
Carton	That's well, I have known such energy as yours do great things before now – but never such great things as this. But try!
Manette	I will go to the prosecutor and the President straight away.
Carton	May you prosper.

Manette leaves.

Lorry	I have no hope.
Carton	Nor have I.
Lorry	Even if either of those men were disposed to spare him, I doubt whether they dare after the demonstration in the court.
Carton	So do I. I heard the fall of the axe in that noise. Don't despair. Don't grieve. I encouraged Doctor Manette in the idea because I felt that one day it might be some consolation to Lucie. Otherwise she might think her husband's life wantonly thrown away or wasted, and that might trouble her.
Lorry	Yes, yes, you are right. But he will perish; there is no real hope.
Carton	Yes, he will perish; there is no real hope. We must prepare for the worst. (*He produces a piece of paper*) This is a certificate which enables me to pass out of the city. You see – Sydney Carton, an Englishman. Keep it for me until tomorrow. (*He produces another*) This is a similar certificate for Doctor Manette. It enables him and his daughter to leave. It is good until it is recalled, which I have reason to think it will be.
Lorry	Manette and Lucie are in danger?

Carton	Great danger. They are in danger of being denounced by Madame Defarge. I learnt as much from Miss Pross' excellent brother, Citizen Barsad. Don't look so horrified, you will save them.
Lorry	Heaven grant I may, Carton. But how?
Carton	You have money and can buy the means of travelling to the coast. Have your horses ready at two o'clock in the afternoon.
Lorry	It shall be done!
Carton	You have a noble heart. Tell Lucie tonight that you know of danger to her and her father. Press upon her the necessity of leaving Paris at two. Tell her that was her husband's last arrangement. Tell her more depends upon it than she dare believe or hope. You think her father will submit to her?
Lorry	If he fails to save Charles, Heaven knows what his state of mind will be; but he will do as Lucie wishes, I am sure of it.
Carton	Have all these arrangements made, even to the taking of your own seat in the carriage. The moment I come to you, take me in and drive away.
Lorry	I wait for you under all circumstances?
Carton	Wait for nothing but to have my place occupied, and then for England!

Manette enters. He is confused and faltering.

Manette	I cannot find it, and I must have it. Where is it? Where is my bench. I have been looking everywhere for my bench and I can't find it.

Lorry motions Carton to be quiet.

Manette	What have they done with my work? Time presses; I must finish those shoes.

Carton and Lorry exchange glances. They know Manette has failed in his quest.

Manette Give me my work. What is to become of us, if those shoes are not done tonight?

Carton He has failed. The last chance is gone; it was not much. Promise me now that you will stick to every detail of the plan we have just agreed.

Lorry I shall, Carton.

Carton Remember those words tomorrow. If you change the plan, or delay, for any reason, no life can possibly be saved, and many lives will inevitably be sacrificed.

Lorry I will remember them. I hope to do my part faithfully.

Carton And I hope to do mine. Now, goodbye!

Carton leaves. Lorry moves to comfort Manette.
Blackout

· ·

Scene 6

The Defarges' wine shop. The Citizens sit drinking. Jacques 2 is speaking with The Vengeance. Defarge and Mme Defarge are at the bar.

Jacques 2 It is true what madame says; why stop? There is great force in that. Why stop?

Defarge One must stop somewhere. The question is, where?

Mme Defarge At extermination!

The Vengeance Magnificent!

Defarge Extermination is a good doctrine, my wife, in general I say nothing against it. But this doctor has suffered much; you observed his face when the paper was read.

Mme Defarge	Yes, I have observed his face. I observed his face to be not the face of a true friend of the Republic. Let him take care of his face.
Defarge	And you have observed the anguish of his daughter.
Mme Defarge	Yes, I have observed her in the court. I have observed her more times than one. Let me but lift my finger and...

She makes a chopping motion with her hand.

Jacques 2	The citizeness is superb!
The Vengeance	She is an angel!
Mme Defarge	(*To her husband*) As to you. If it depended on you, which happily it does not, you would rescue Evrémonde even now.
Defarge	No I would not. But I would leave the matter there. I say stop!
Mme Defarge	See you then, Jacques and see you too, my little Vengeance. Listen! For other crimes as tyrants and oppressors, I have this race a long time on my register. (*She shows her knitting to them*) Doomed to destruction and extermination. Ask my husband is that so?
Defarge	It is so.
Mme Defarge	I have reason. Is it so?
Defarge	It is so.
Citizen 5	And Thérèse Defarge tells her reason.
Citizen 6	Thérèse Defarge tells her secret.
Citizen 5	The peasant family injured by the Evrémondes...
Mme Defarge	...was my family!
Citizen 5	The sister of the wounded boy on the ground...

Mme Defarge	. . . was my sister!
Citizen 6	The husband worked to death . . .
Mme Defarge	. . . was my sister's husband!
Citizen 5	The brother run through by the Evrémonde's sword . . .
Mme Defarge	. . . was my brother!
Citizen 6	The father killed by heartbreak . . .
Mme Defarge	. . . was my father. Those dead were my dead!
Citizen 5	The right to vengeance belongs to Thérèse Defarge.
Mme Defarge	Is that so?
Citizens 5 and 6	It is so.
Mme Defarge	Then tell the wind and fire where to stop, but don't tell me!

Defarge shakes his head and goes out.

Mme Defarge	My husband is a good Republican and a bold man; but he has his weaknesses. He would show mercy to this doctor.
The Vengeance	It is a great pity. It is a thing to regret.
Mme Defarge	I care nothing for the doctor, he may wear his head or lose it. But the Evrémonde people are to be exterminated and the wife must follow the husband.
Jacques 2	She has a fine head for it. Golden hair and blue eyes!
Mme Defarge	In a word I cannot trust my husband. I must act for myself. But can I spare the doctor to my husband?
The Vengeance	He would count as one head. We do not have enough heads.
Mme Defarge	Then he must take his chance, I cannot spare him! The wife of Evrémonde will be at home now awaiting the moment of his death. She will be mourning and grieving for him. She will be

in a state of mind to cry out against the Republic. She will be full of sympathy with its enemies. I will go to her. If I delay, I fear there is a danger that she might escape.

The Vengeance   What an admirable woman!

Mme Defarge   (*To The Vengeance*) Take my knitting and have it ready for me at my usual seat.

The Vengeance   You will not be late?

Mme Defarge   I will be there before the tumbrils arrive!

Mme Defarge leaves.

The Vengeance   What an adorable woman!

Blackout.

· ·

Scene 7

The upstage raised area is now Darnay's prison cell. It contains a table, (bearing paper, ink and a quill) and a chair. Darnay sits on the chair. The Citizens observe him.

Citizen 1   In the black prison of the Conciergerie.

Citizen 2   The doomed of the day await their fate.

Citizen 3   Fifty-two heads are to roll today.

Citizen 4   A head for every week of the year.

Citizen 5	Charles Darnay, formerly Evrémonde, alone in his cell, knows nothing will save him.
Citizen 6	Clocks strike the numbers he will never hear again.

A clock slowly strikes twelve, then one.

Citizen 7	Nine gone forever.
Citizen 8	Ten gone forever.
Citizen 1	Eleven gone forever.
Citizen 2	Twelve gone forever.
Citizen 3	One gone forever.
Darnay	And now there is but one more hour left.

*The **Citizens** step back into the shadows and exit.*

Barsad	(*Off stage*) Go you in alone. I wait near. Lose no time!

*Darnay starts as **Carton** walks in. **Carton** puts his finger to his lips.*

Carton	Of all the people upon earth, you least expected to see me?
Darnay	I could not believe it to be you. You are not a prisoner?
Carton	No, I am in power over one of the keepers here. I come from her – your wife, dear Darnay. I bring a request from her.
Darnay	What is it?
Carton	She begs you to do as I tell you. You have no time to ask me why I bring this message, or what it means. You must obey. Take off those boots you wear and put on these of mine.

*Carton takes off his boots and hands them over to **Darnay**.*

Darnay	Carton, there is no escaping from this place. It is madness.
Carton	It would be madness if I asked you to escape, but do I? Change this cravat for mine and put on my coat.

Darnay does so, reluctantly.

Darnay	Carton, dear Carton, to think of escape is madness. It cannot be accomplished.
Carton	Do I ask you to pass the door? When I ask that refuse. There are ink and paper on the table. Write what I dictate. Quick friend, quick!

Darnay turns to the table and takes up a quill.

Carton	Write exactly as I speak.
Darnay	To whom do I address it?
Carton	To no one.

Carton stands over Darnay. As he dictates, Carton draws out a handkerchief and a small medicine bottle from his pocket. He empties the contents of the bottle into the handkerchief.

Carton	(*Dictating*) You will remember the words that passed between us long ago. I am thankful that the time has come when I can prove them.

Darnay stops, looks up and sniffs the air.

Darnay	What vapour is that?
Carton	I am conscious of no vapour. Take up the pen and finish. Hurry!

Darnay returns to the paper.

Carton	Do not grieve that I have at last found a purpose for my life...

*As he says these final words, **Carton**
smothers **Darnay** with the handkerchief.
There is a brief struggle, before **Darnay**
slumps into unconsciousness.*

Carton   (*Calling out*) Enter! Come in!

***Barsad** enters.*

Barsad   (*Checking Darnay*) Sleeping like a babe in arms. For how long?

Carton   For several hours. You see, is your hazard very great?

Barsad   Mr Carton, I am in no danger if you are true to your bargain.

Carton   Have no fear, I shall soon be out of the way of harming you.
                  Now take me to the coach.

Barsad   You?

Carton   Him, man, with whom I have exchanged. I was weak when you
                  brought me here and am fainter. Now take me out! Take him
                  to the courtyard you know of, place him in the carriage, show
                  him to Mr Lorry. Tell that gentleman to give him air and to
                  remember my words of last night and his promise. I hear the
                  jailer! Hurry, man!

***Barsad** picks up **Darnay**, drags him to the
door and exits. **Carton** is left alone.*

Jailer   (*Off stage*) Evrémonde!

*The **jailer** enters.*

Jailer   Evrémonde. It is time.

Blackout.

. . . .

Scene 8

In one of the downstage areas, **Miss Pross** *busies herself with packing a trunk. There is a movement that makes her start.* **Mme Defarge** *has entered the room.*

Miss Pross   Are the horses ready, Mr ... (*She sees Mme Defarge*) ... oh!

Mme Defarge   The wife of Evrémonde. Where is she? I am come to pay my compliments. I wish to see her.

Miss Pross   I know your intentions are evil and you may depend upon it, I'll hold my own against them.

Mme Defarge   It will do her no good to keep herself concealed from me. Go tell her I wish to see her.

Miss Pross   (*To herself*) I know that the longer I keep you here, the greater hope there is for my ladybird. (*To Mme Defarge*) You might from your appearance be the wife of Lucifer, nevertheless you will not get the better of me. I am an Englishwoman!

Mme Defarge   Woman imbecile. I take no answer from you. I demand to see her. Citizen Doctor! Wife of Evrémonde! Answer the Citizeness Defarge! (*She sees the trunk*) There has been hurried packing! She is not here! Ha! They can be pursued!

Miss Pross grabs Mme Defarge to stop her leaving. **Mme Defarge** *pulls a pistol from her belt. The struggle continues; the pistol fires –* **Mme Defarge** *falls to the ground, dead.* **Miss Pross** *appears dazed.* **Cruncher** *enters.*

Cruncher   What's happened here? (*He sees the body and reacts*) My Lord ...

Miss Pross   I don't hear you. What do you say?

Cruncher   Deaf! Deaf in an instant. (*He beckons to her*) Miss Pross, it's time to go.

Miss Pross   I can't hear you. I don't think I shall ever hear again.

Cruncher	We must go! They will be at the barrier by now. Once through that, nothing can stop them. (*Pause*) If they *get* through ...

> ***Cruncher*** *bustles* ***Miss Pross*** *off stage.*
> *Blackout. In the darkness a voice is heard.*

Citizen 5	Who goes there? Papers!

> *The lights come up slowly on the other downstage area. It is the city barrier, guarded by the* ***Citizens***. *The lights brighten to reveal* ***Lorry***, ***Manette***, ***Lucie*** *and* ***Darnay*** *inside a carriage.* ***Manette*** *is rocking back and forward.* ***Darnay*** *lies slumped.*
> ***Citizen 5*** *steps forward.* ***Lorry*** *hands the certificates to him.*

Citizen 5	(*Peering into the carriage*) Alexandre Manette. Physician. French. Which is he?

> ***Lorry*** *points out Manette.*

Citizen 5	Apparently the doctor is not in his right mind? Revolution fever been too much for him?

> *The other* ***Citizens*** *laugh.*

Citizen 6	Many suffer from it!
Citizen 5	Lucie. His daughter. French. Which is she?

> ***Lorry*** *points out Lucie.*

Citizen 5	The wife of Evrémonde, is it not?
Lorry	It is.
Citizen 6	Hah! *He* has an appointment elsewhere!

> *The* ***Citizens*** *laugh again.*

Citizen 5	Sydney Carton. Lawyer. English. Which is he?

*Lorry points out Darnay. The **Citizens** inspect the carriage, looking hard and long at Darnay.*

Citizen 5   He is not well?

Lorry   Alas, he is not in good health and has separated from a friend who is under the displeasure of the Republic.

Citizen 5   Is that all? Many are under the displeasure of the Republic.

Citizen 6   He is like the emigrant, Evrémonde.

Citizen 5   Fool! All the world knows of the resemblance between this Englishman and Evrémonde; did you not see him in Citizen Defarge's wine shop?

Citizen 6   I dare swear Evrémonde wishes himself here now!

*The **Citizens** laugh again.*

Citizen 5   Jarvis Lorry. Banker. English. That is you?

Lorry   That is me.

Citizen 5   Your papers, Jarvis Lorry.

Lorry   One can depart, citizen?

Citizen 5   One can depart. A good journey!

Lorry   I salute you citizens! To England!

Blackout.

. . . .

Scene 9

A group of aristocrats enter. They stand ready to mount the scaffold. A clock strikes two. A jailer enters with Carton.

Jailer   Follow me, Evrémonde!

> *He leads **Carton** to join the condemned. A **girl** steps forward from the group of prisoners.*

Girl   Citizen Evrémonde. I am a poor seamstress, who was with you in La Force.

Carton   True. I forget what you were accused of.

Girl   Plots. Though I am innocent of any. Is it likely? Who would think of plotting with a poor creature like me? I am not afraid to die, Citizen Evrémonde, but I have done nothing. I am not unwilling to die, if the Republic which is to do so much good to us poor will profit by my death; but I do not know how that will be, Citizen Evrémonde. I heard you were released, I hoped it was true.

Carton   It was. But I was taken again and condemned.

Girl   If I may ride with you, will you let me hold your hand? I am not afraid, but I am little and weak and it will give me courage.

> *She looks up at Carton and lets out a gasp. **Carton** puts his finger to his lips.*

Girl	(*Whispering*) Are you dying for him?
Carton	And his wife. Yes. Hush!
Girl	Will you let me hold your brave hand, stranger?
Carton	Yes, my poor sister. To the last.

> *The **Citizens** and other spectators,*
> *including **The Vengeance**, enter and line*
> *the 'street'. **Carton**, the **girl** and the other*
> *prisoners stand in line awaiting their turn.*
> *In the background the shadow of the*
> *guillotine looms large.*

Citizen 1	Along the Paris streets, the death carts rumble hollow and harsh...
Citizen 3	...carrying the day's wine to La Guillotine.
Citizen 4	Fifty-two heads...
Citizen 6	...fifty-two cheers.
Citizen 5	Down with Evrémonde!
Citizen 7	All aristocrats to the guillotine.
Citizen 8	Death to the traitor Evrémonde!
The Vengeance	Thérèse! Who has seen Thérèse Defarge?
Citizen 2	She never missed before.
The Vengeance	Nor will she now. Thérèse! Bad fortune! Here the guillotine is ready and Evrémonde will be despatched in a wink! Thérèse! Thérèse Defarge!

> ***The Vengeance's*** *cries are cut off by a*
> *cheer as the guillotine comes down and*
> *dispatches a victim. She leaves in search of*
> *Mme Defarge.*
> ***Carton*** *and the **girl** move forward.*

Girl	But for you dear stranger, I should not be so composed. I think you were sent to me by Heaven.
Carton	Or you to me. Keep your eyes upon me and mind no other object.
Girl	I mind nothing while I hold your hand. I shall mind nothing when I let it go, if they are rapid.
Carton	They will be rapid. Fear not!

A cheer goes up as the guillotine takes another victim.

Girl	Brave friend, will you let me ask one question? I have a cousin five years younger than I and she lives in a house in the South. Poverty parted us and she knows nothing of my fate. I have been thinking as we came along; if the Republic really does good to the poor, and they come to be less hungry and suffer less, she may live to grow old.

Another victim, another cheer.

Carton	What then, gentle sister?
Girl	Do you think that it will seem a long time while I wait for her in the better land where I trust both you and I will be mercifully sheltered?
Carton	It cannot be, my child. There is no time there, and no trouble there.
Girl	You comfort me so much! I am so ignorant.

There is another cheer.

Girl	Am I to kiss you now? Is the moment come?
Carton	Yes.

Carton kisses the girl on the lips. He releases her hand. She steps through the crowd towards the guillotine and disappears.

> *Drums roll before the guillotine despatches her. The **Citizens** cheer. **Carton** readies himself for his sacrifice.*

Citizen 1 It is a far, far better thing you do now, than you have ever done.

> ***Carton** begins to move forward. He goes through the crowd and exits unseen.*

All Citizens It is a far, far better rest that you go to than you have ever known.

> *The drums roll. The guillotine flashes down.*
> *Snap blackout.*

Activities

About the Author

Charles Dickens was born at Portsmouth on February 7th 1812. His father was hopeless with money and was sent to prison for debt when Dickens was twelve years old. Young Charles had to leave school and go and work in a factory. He never forgot this dreadful experience and later created characters in his novels, like David Copperfield and Nicholas Nickleby, who become poor and miserable either because their parents got into debt or died. Dickens managed to return to school for a couple of years and from there he got a job working as an office boy in a law office. He then became a county reporter and eventually he reported on the debates in parliament for *The Morning Chronicle*.

About 1833, Dickens began to write stories about unusual characters which were eventually published as *Sketches by Boz* (Boz was his pen-name) in 1836. This was followed by his first popular success, *The Pickwick Papers*, published also in 1836. This made Dickens famous in four months. *Oliver Twist* followed in 1837, and *Nicholas Nickleby* shortly afterwards. All these novels were first published in magazine episodes and Dickens had to work hard to meet his deadlines. In fact, the books were written like episodes of a modern television soap opera.

Dickens married Catherine Hogarth in 1836. Their marriage was not a happy one and, although they had ten children, they separated in 1858. Dickens did have a love affair with Ellen Ternan, an actress, and this probably brought his already unhappy marriage to an end. He was a man of many talents: he edited periodicals, he lectured in America, and he managed a theatre company. He also wrote a lot more novels, many of them taking as their theme social injustices in Victorian society. His last novel, *The Mystery of Edwin Drood*, was left unfinished when he died in 1870.

Research

1 Find out more about the life of Charles Dickens.

2 Dickens wrote fourteen major novels and many shorter stories. Try and find out about some of them.

3 He also created some of the most famous characters in English literature. Find out in which books some of the following characters appear:

- Ebeneezer Scrooge
- Fagin
- Mr Macawber
- Mr Pickwick
- Miss Haversham
- The Artful Dodger
- Little Nell
- Mr Squeers

. . . .

A Tale of Two Cities

Read

A Tale of Two Cities was published in weekly parts between April 30th and November 26th 1859. It is the only one of Dickens' novels where most of the action takes place in a country other than England and it is perhaps the most eventful and romantic of all his works. Dickens got his background information about Paris and the French Revolution from a book written by his friend Thomas Carlisle called *The French Revolution*.

When Dickens wrote **A Tale of Two Cities**, he considered several alternative titles before he made up his mind. The other titles he considered were:

- Buried Alive
- The Golden Thread
- Memory Carton

The novel was also performed as a play in the early Twentieth century with the title: *The Only Way*.

Discuss

Why do you think these titles were considered?

Talk and Write

Choosing a New Title
1 In groups make some suggestions for a new title for the playscript.
2 From your suggestions choose the one that your group thinks is best.
3 As a class, make a list of these new titles.
4 Each group should then explain why they chose the title.
5 The class can then vote for the most appropriate new title.

Design

Design a Cover
1 Design a cover for the playscript using the new title.
2 Imagine that your school has decided to use this playscript for its school production. Design posters and programmes using the new title. When designing all these things try to think of images that reflect the main issues raised in the play, as well as the main events and the characters.

Picturing the Scene
The following pictures are taken from the original novel. They are by
Hablot L. Browne who was also known as 'Phiz'.

Discuss   1   From which parts of **A Tale of Two Cities** are these pictures taken?
           2   Which scenes would you place them in? Explain why.

Draw   Draw your own illustration for a particular scene in the playscript. You
                may need to do some research into the following things:

- **Clothing:** worn by the French aristocrats and the revolutionaries;
  what about the English characters? How would theirs be different
  from the two groups already mentioned?
- **Places:** the Bastille, a French château, a house in a poor district of
  Paris, a prison cell.
- **Objects:** a guillotine, a tumbril, a carriage, shoemaking equipment.

. . . .

The French Revolution

Read

At the time that Dickens wrote **A Tale of Two Cities** many people believed that the French Revolution happened because the working class people of France, after years of hunger and paying high taxes to the rich aristocrats (including the King and Queen), rebelled against the system, guillotined all the aristocrats and overthrew the monarchy. The remark 'Let them eat cake', supposedly made by Queen Marie Antoinette, when she was told that the poor people had no bread to eat, is one many people recognize. It seems to support the view of the French Revolution as a class war, between the aristocrats and the peasants.

Historians now believe that the reasons for the French Revolution were much more complicated and that the revolutionary movement was actually led by a group of people who were well-educated and influenced by new ideas. Many of these people were lawyers and writers. Others were nobles who did not agree with the old ways of the aristocracy.

Dickens' story is based on the struggle between the rich and the poor. The aristocrats are represented by the Marquis of Evrémonde and his brother and the working class by the Defarges and to a lesser extent the Jacques, The Vengeance, and Gaspard. The young woman and her brother, who are victims of the Evrémonde family, are examples of country peasants treated badly by the nobility.

The events of the French Revolution are complex and Dickens chose to include certain incidents which are historically accurate to assist his storyline. Below is a list of dates of historical events which are relevant to the action of the playscript. Beside each date is a reference to the relevant scene in the playscript.

1789   ●   On July 14th, the Bastille prison (a symbol of the power of the aristocracy) in the Saint-Antoine district of Paris was stormed by an angry mob. (*Act 1, Scene 5*)

       ●   In August, those sympathetic to the Revolution issued the Declaration of the Rights of Man. The motto of the Revolution became 'Liberty, Equality and Fraternity'. (*Act 2, Scene 1*)

1792   ●   A vote was taken and carried to abolish the monarchy. The guillotine was used to execute those who continued to support the King and Queen and the old way of life of the aristocracy. (*Act 1, Scene 6*)

1793   ●   On January 21st, Louis XVI was executed. (*Act 2, Scene 2*)

       ●   In March the Revolutionary Tribunals were set up to try those accused of opposing the aims of the Revolution. (*Act 2, Scenes 3 and 5*)

- In September the Law of Suspects came into force which allowed for the arrest of all those people who might be a threat to the Revolution. (*Act 2, Scene 1*)
- In October Queen Marie Antoinette was sent to the guillotine. Her hair is said to have gone grey during her time in prison. (*Act 2, Scene 2*)

The years that followed 1793 saw several men lead the Revolution including Robespierre whose time in power is known as 'The Reign of Terror'. After his execution in 1794, other groups or factions took charge. Towards the end of 1799, General Napoleon Bonaparte rose to power. He was popular in France due to his success during the recent wars with Europe. He became Emperor of France and ruled as a dictator until his downfall in 1814.

Research

1   Try to find out more about the following:

- the sansculottes
- the storming of the Bastille
- Louis XVI and Marie Antoinette
- the tricolour (flag)
- Robespierre
- Jean Paul Marat and Charlotte Corday

2   What do the words Liberty, Equality and Fraternity mean?

3   What happens in modern France on Bastille Day?

. . . .

Two Worlds: the Aristocrats and the Revolutionaries
Defarge and Madame Defarge are Revolutionaries, but their beliefs and
actions are not identical.

Discuss

Compare these two characters and their approach to the Revolution.

1   Defarge represents the more moderate wing of the revolutionary
     movement. Find evidence in the play to support this view.

2   Madame Defarge's commitment to bloodshed is absolute. Look for
     evidence in the play that she represents the more extreme elements of the
     Revolution.

*Talk and
Write*

The Marquis of Evrémonde is an aristocrat with a large château in the
country. Gaspard lives in poverty in the Saint-Antoine district of Paris.
The peasant woman and her brother from Act 2, Scene 5 live in the
village by the Marquis' château.

1   Look at the Prologue, Scene 2 and make notes about the place where
     Gaspard lives. Then, go back to the play to re-read Act 1, Scene 2 and
     Act 2, Scene 5 to find out what it was like to be a peasant in the country
     where the aristocrat's power was absolute. Make some notes on this too.

2   Look again at Act 1, Scene 2 and make notes about the lifestyle of the
     Marquis. You might also want to look at the end of this scene where the
     Marquis and Darnay discuss their different views on how an aristocrat
     should behave.

3   From these notes, what is your impression of what life is like for the poor
     in both the city and the country?

4   Using your notes and observations, make a list to compare and contrast
     the lives of the rich and the poor. Set it out in two columns: one headed
     'rich' and one headed 'poor'.

Discuss

1   Which group of people does Dickens approve of most? The world of
     revolutionary Paris or the world of the privileged aristocrats?

2   Does he find something to admire in both societies?

3   Does he find something to criticize in both societies?
     Look for evidence in the play. It may help to consider these questions:

●   Darnay is an aristocrat. Is he bad? What would life be like if all
     nobles were like him?

●   Madame Defarge and The Vengeance support the Revolution. Is all
     their behaviour acceptable? What about Madame Defarge's plans for
     Lucie?

●   How do you feel about the aristocrats that Darnay encounters in
     prison (Act 2, Scene 1)? Is it possible to feel sorry for them?

Newspapers

Read

During the Revolution many underground newspapers were published and writers both for and against the revolutionary movement wrote articles and pamphlets which were circulated in Paris.

Write

1   Imagine that you are producing an underground newspaper the day after the storming of the Bastille. Decide whether you are pro-revolution or pro-aristocracy. Design the front page and write an article about the events of July 14th 1789. You may need to do some further research and you may also find it helpful to read the relevant chapters of the novel: 'Echoing Footsteps' and 'The Sea Still Rises'.

2   You may also choose to write a report of the events at Darnay's second appearance before the Tribunal (Act 2, Scene 5). You could concentrate on Doctor Manette's evidence concerning the Marquis of Evrémonde and his brother. Again, decide if your paper supports the revolutionaries or the aristocracy.

The Law of Suspects

Read

The Law of Suspects was passed on September 17th 1793. This was the law under which Darnay was arrested and tried.

The Law of Suspects
1793

1. Immediately after the publication of this decree, all suspects found on the territory of the Republic and who are still at liberty will be arrested.
2. Suspects are
(i) Those who, either by their conduct or their relationships, by their conversation or by their writing, are shown to be partisans of tyranny and federalism and enemies of liberty;
(ii) Those who cannot justify, under the provisions of the law of 21 March last, their means of existence and the performance of their civic duties;
(iii) Those who have been refused certificates of civic responsibility;
(iv) Public officials suspended or deprived of their functions by the National Convention or its agents, and not since reinstated, especially those who have been, or ought to be, dismissed by the law of 12 August last;
(v) Those former nobles, including husbands, wives, fathers, mothers, sons or daughters, brothers or sisters, and agents of emigres, who have not constantly manifested their loyalty to the Revolution;
(vi) Those who have emigrated during the interval between the 1 July 1789 and the publication of the law of 8 April 1792, although they may have returned to France during the period of delay fixed by the law or before.

Talk and Write

1. Which of the six clauses above allowed Darnay to be arrested and sent to prison? (There may be more than one.)
2. Why did Darnay return to France? List the reasons.
3. Was he right to return to France? Give your opinion on this.
4. Do you think he knew about the dangers? (Look at Act 2, Scene 1.)
5. Give reasons why you think he should have stayed in England.

Write

Write a short scene, set out like a playscript, in which Darnay explains to Lucie why he must go back to France. How does she react? What questions does she ask and what answers does he give?

Characters

Connections
There are many different links between the characters in **A Tale of Two Cities**.

Talk and Write

Draw a diagram to show the way the characters are connected. You may wish to make a large copy of this and display it on the classroom wall. This connections diagram has been started for you. Add the following characters:

- Mr Lorry
- Jerry Cruncher
- Marquis of Evrémonde
- John Barsad
- Gabelle
- The Vengeance

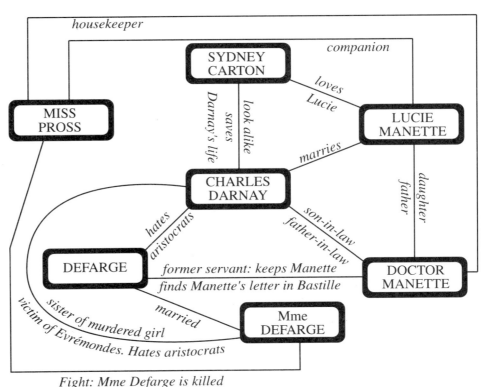

Fight: Mme Defarge is killed

. . . .

Talk and
Write

Character Studies

1   Choose three characters from the playscript.
2   Make a list of words which describe them.
3   Then, look for examples from the playscript to back-up your description. For example: if you think that Darnay is brave, find an incident from the play that supports this viewpoint.

Talk and
Write

Comparing Characters

Look at the following pairs of characters. In what ways are they different? Use evidence from the playscript to make notes on each pair. Compare what they do, where they live, how they think, and how they behave towards other people.

- Sydney Carton and Charles Darnay
- John Barsad and Jarvis Lorry
- Doctor Manette and the Marquis of Evrémonde
- Miss Pross and Madame Defarge

Talk and
Write

Heroism

1   What qualities should a hero have? Make a list of them.
2   Who are your heroes? These can be real people or characters from books or films.
3   Why do you admire them?
4   Is there a hero in **A Tale of Two Cities**? If you think there is, who is it? Give your reasons for choosing that person. Do they have any of the hero qualities from your list?
5   Look through the play and make a list of heroic actions. These may be performed by characters other than the person you have chosen as the hero of the play. You should look closely at the actions of some of the minor characters.

Discuss

Sacrifice

1   Why do you think Sydney Carton gives up his life in order to save
    Charles Darnay, who was his rival for Lucie's love?

2   Try to find some evidence from the play to support your reasons. You
    might want to look at the following scenes: Act 1, Scene 1; Act 1,
    Scene 3; Act 2, Scene 7.

3   Is Carton right to sacrifice his life?

Discuss

1   Can you think of modern examples of people sacrificing their life for
    someone else or for something that they believe in?

2   Is there anything you would die for?

    ● Your friends?
    ● Your parents?
    ● Your brothers and sisters?
    ● Other relatives?
    ● Your country?
    ● A cause such as Human Rights or Animal Rights?

Write

1   Imagine that you are Lucie. Write a letter to your husband, Charles
    Darnay, who is in prison in Paris. What news would you give him? How
    could you comfort him?

2   Imagine that you are Doctor Manette. Write a letter to the Revolutionary
    Council in Paris asking them to spare the life of your son-in-law, Charles
    Darnay. What reasons would you give to persuade them to release him?

3   Imagine that you are Miss Pross. You have returned home from Paris.
    Write a letter to a friend in England describing the events that took place
    while you were in France.

    Try to copy the way each character would write (or speak) in your
    letters. You may also find the drama techniques (particularly hot seating)
    outlined on pages 150–151 useful as a starting point.

Drama

You can use the following drama techniques to help you explore the play further.

Improvisation
You are given a situation to work on in groups. Using your own words, you act out a scene which shows what you think about this subject. There are two main types of improvisation.

Planned: in this you are given time to prepare your work by talking with your friends and trying out your ideas. When you have practised your work and are satisfied with it, you show it to other people.

Instant: in this you are given a character and a situation, but you are not given any time to prepare. You must start the improvisation straight away.

Improvise 1   Improvise a scene in which someone takes the blame for something a friend has done, or has been wrongly accused of doing.

2   Imagine that you are awaiting execution. Work out a monologue in which you speak your last thoughts as your final minutes slip away. You could do this in role as one of the characters from **A Tale of Two Cities**, for example: Sydney Carton, the young seamstress (Act 2, Scene 9), Gaspard as he hangs in his cage from the walls of the château (Act 1, Scene 4) or you could invent your own character.

Still Image
A still image is like a photograph. Any number of people may be in the image. A situation is chosen and the group must produce a frozen picture as if they had been captured on film by a photographer. You may wish to choose just one image, or use a series of images to tell a story.

Thought Tapping
This helps us to understand what the characters in a still image are thinking. In turn, each member of the group says what their character was thinking at the moment the 'photograph' was taken.

Still Image 1   In groups of four or five, choose three different moments from the play and create a still image for each of these.

Thought Tapping 2   Give each character in the image a thought that they are thinking at the moment captured by the image. Show the rest of the class. Can they guess who your characters are and which part of the play your image comes from? How did they work it out?

Hot Seating

When a member of the group has played, or is about to play a character in an improvisation, a role play or a written play, they can be put in the 'hot seat'. This means that other members of the group can ask them questions, and they must answer them **in the character** of their chosen person.

Hot Seating

1   Prepare a list of questions to ask Darnay, Lucie, Doctor Manette, Lorry, and Miss Pross on their return to England. You may want to use the questions below as a starting point:

- How do they view Carton's sacrifice?
- Should he have done it?
- What does Lucie think of Carton?
- Has Darnay changed his view of Carton?

2   Choose members of the class to take the roles of Lucie, Darnay, Doctor Manette, Lorry and Miss Pross and 'hot seat' them.

What the Adapters Say

Adapting a novel into a play is rather like doing a very long and complicated summary exercise. There is no 'right' way to do it, and nobody will ever achieve a 'perfect' adaptation, because when you read a novel you use your imagination to fill out what the author does not tell you and to interpret what he or she does. We chose to adapt **A Tale of Two Cities** because it has a good story, strong characters, and a dramatic plot which centres on one of the great events of history; and also because it was written by one of the world's great storytellers, Charles Dickens.

Length
The most obvious task of the adapter is to reduce the book's length; after all, it would take even a pretty fast reader at least a week to read the novel properly, while no audience is happily going to stay seated in a theatre for more than three hours.

Plots
Because they are long and complex stories, novels tend to have a main plot and several sub-plots. In **A Tale of Two Cities**, the main plot is the relationship between Charles Darnay, Lucie Manette and Sydney Carton. All the other plots add interest and help provide fuel to drive the main story, but they are sidelines. Some sub-plots are essential to the story and some are not. For example, the lawyer Stryver is important in that he successfully defends Darnay against a false charge of treason (the book would have been rather short if Darnay had been hanged at this point!). But in the novel, Stryver decides he wants to marry Lucie. This leads to complications that are very funny, but they are not actually essential to the main story, so we decided not to use this plotline in the adaptation.

Dialogue
In writing this adaptation, we used many of Dickens' own words. This is because Dickens wrote very theatrical dialogue. He was an amateur actor and had a great love of the theatre, and his dialogue works very well on stage.
However, we had to shorten some of the dialogue, or the play would go on too long. In a novel, people can speak at length without losing the reader's interest, but this is not the case with a character on stage, who has to speak as briefly as possible without losing the sense of the words. For example: after Darnay has been acquitted (Act 1, Scene 1), Stryver proposes that he and Carton drink a toast to Lucie Manette. In the novel, the dialogue reads as follows (Stryver speaks first):

'The picturesque doctor's daughter, Miss Manette.'
'She pretty?'
'Is she not?'
'No.'
'Why, man, she was the admiration of the whole court!'
'Rot the admiration of the whole court! Who made the Old Bailey a judge of beauty? She was a golden-haired doll!'

We adapted this as:

Stryver	The picturesque doctor's daughter, Miss Manette.
Carton	She pretty?
Stryver	Is she not?
Carton	She's a golden-haired doll!

This means very much the same. Carton needs more words in the book to make us understand his pretended dislike of Lucie, but when we can see the actor on stage we can 'read' a great deal from his manner, the tone of his voice, his gestures; none of which we can see on the page of a book.

Narration
Vital information often appears in the narration (that is, the description of what is happening in the story). Sometimes, for instance when the scene is being set, the original narration appears in the adaptation as instructions to the actors (stage directions):

Prologue:
Scene 1
England: the Dover road, just outside London. Barrels, boxes and hampers are placed downstage to represent a mail coach. It is the early hours of the morning and as the lights come up, they reveal **Lucie Manette, Mr Jarvis Lorry, Miss Pross** *and several coach passengers, muffled against the cold and half-asleep. The* **coachman** *(Tom) and the* **guard** *(Joe) are sitting at each end of the coach. They are surrounded by the eight* **Citizens**.

In these few lines we have tried to set the scene as Dickens sets it in the first few pages of Chapter 2 of Book 1, 'The Mail'. The rest is up to the actors.
At other times it is possible for the actors to convey information given in the narration by the way they react to what is said. 'Lucie gasped' or 'Darnay was disconcerted', might also be given as bracketed stage directions:

Lucie	(*Gasps*) Oh, Charles, is that you?
Darnay	(*Disconcerted*) Of course. Were you expecting someone else?

Other narration can be conveyed by lighting ('It was night', 'One bright morning', etc), setting, sound effects or other means. However, some of it has to be included in the dialogue; so the adapter has to give the characters lines never written by the author of the novel. These new lines must blend in with the original dialogue without appearing out of place or out of character.

We decided to give much of the narrative to a chorus of 'Citizens' who move between the two cities of London and Paris. A chorus was first used in the dramas of ancient Greece, to comment on the action and ask the main characters questions. Many plays (including several of Shakespeare's) feature a narrator, as do several modern musicals, such as *Blood Brothers* and *The Rocky Horror Show*, but we decided to have several narrators. We also decided that our narrators should be characters too, able to step into the action (as when they become Old Bailey lawyers prosecuting Darnay [Act 1, Scene 1]) or out of it (as when they read Mr Lorry's letter over Lucie's shoulder [Prologue, Scene 1]). The chorus therefore works as a link between the audience and the play. The Citizens are sometimes audience, and sometimes actors, but mostly somewhere in between. For this reason, they can talk directly to the audience, as the actors cannot.

Time
The events of the novel take place between 1775, when Lucie finds Doctor Manette, and 1794 when Carton is executed. This is long enough for Darnay and Lucie to get married and have two children: a boy, who dies in infancy, and little Lucie, who does not appear in the adaptation. Events move slowly; for instance, Darnay is imprisoned for over a year in Paris before his trial.

We have chosen to indicate only major passages of time; apart from this, the action appears to take only a few weeks. The biggest liberty we took with time was staging the wedding of Darnay and Lucie and the storming of the Bastille together, with each event interrupting the other. This makes a highly dramatic scene, with the peace and joy of the wedding contrasting with the hatred and terror of the invasion of the Bastille. It also enabled us to place the Defarges' discovery that Doctor Manette was sent to the Bastille by the Evrémonde family, and Darnay's admission to Manette that he, too, is an Evrémonde, in the same moment of time within the play.

Unfortunately, this creates a new timeline for the play which is different to the novel. The actual time scheme of the novel is (approximately) as follows:

1775 Lucie Manette meets her father for the first time
1780 Darnay is tried for treason
1782 marriage of Charles Darnay and Lucie Manette
1789 storming of the Bastille
1792 Gabelle writes to Charles Darnay, who sets off for France
1794 Carton is executed while impersonating Charles Darnay

By 'losing' the seven years between 1782 and 1789, we also lose the character of little Lucie, daughter of Charles and Lucie; but she plays little part in the book except to make us feel even sorrier for Lucie while Darnay is in prison. Dickens himself skips over those seven years in a single chapter.

So, in the playscript, we have 'fudged' the time scale:

- the Citizens tell us that the play begins in 1775
- at Charles Darnay's trial we learn that the action has moved on five years
- Citizen 3 mentions that 'some years have passed' at the beginning of Act 1, Scene 3
- the date (1792) of Gabelle's letter is not given in the adaptation

All this may matter to historians, but not to the play's audience. Time in plays is a sort of 'virtual' time. As long as the order of events is clear, it is not necessary to tell the audience exactly how much time has passed.

Settings

In the novel, there are many changes of scene. Rapid scene changes are fine in books, where all the scenes are in the reader's mind, and in films, where cutting from one scene to another is easy to do and keeps the picture interesting. However, on stage it takes time to change settings and furniture, and while this is being done there is nothing for the audience to do but fidget and get bored. So we have run scenes that take place in different locations into each other. For example, after the mail coach journey at the beginning of the novel, Dickens moves his characters to an inn at Dover. We moved the essential dialogue from the inn scene into the coach scene (Prologue, Scene 1) in order to save having to change the set.

We have also tried to suggest a sort of all-purpose set that can become many different locations without a lot of scene changing. (See A Note on the Set, page 8.)

Cutting

The adapter has to be prepared to be ruthless. Even after you have done all the above, you will still probably find you have a play that would last for about six hours on the stage, and the red pencil has to come out. For example, one of our favourite passages in the book is where Jerry Cruncher's son, young Jerry, discovers that his father is a 'Resurrection Man': that is, he steals newly buried corpses from graveyards and sells them to hospitals for medical students to dissect. Its narrative purpose is to provide Cruncher with evidence against John Barsad. In the novel, Barsad has an accomplice, Roger Cly. It is Cly's corpse that Cruncher tries to dig up, only to find an empty coffin. Carton's discovery that Cly is alive and engaged in spying with Barsad in France is the final 'card' he plays in forcing Barsad to agree to his exchange with Charles Darnay. This is a wonderful scene, both funny and frightening; but it isn't really essential to the plot, and would have made the play too long, so reluctantly we had to let it go.

Read

Adaptation Activity

The extract below comes from the end of the chapter, 'The Honest Tradesman' described above under the heading 'Cutting'. Young Jerry, who has watched his father dig up Cly's coffin, runs home in panic. The next morning, his father and mother fall out about his father's 'business activities'. Cruncher and Young Jerry then set off for the corner of Fleet Street where they wait for messages to carry.

Look at the extract carefully and try to adapt it into a playscript. You will need to write main stage directions, dialogue between the characters and stage directions in brackets to give a character more detailed information on how to say or do something.

Young Jerry, walking with the stool under his arm at his father's side along sunny and crowded Fleet Street, was a very different Young Jerry from him of the previous night, running home through darkness and solitude from his grim pursuer. His cunning was fresh with the day, and his qualms were gone with the night – in which particulars it is not improbable that he had compeers in Fleet Street and the City of London, that fine morning.

'Father,' said Young Jerry, as they walked along: taking care to keep at arm's length and to have the stool well between them: 'what's a resurrection-man?'

Mr Cruncher came to a stop on the pavement before he answered, 'How should I know?'

'I thought you knowed everything, Father,' said the artless boy.

'Hem! Well,' returned Mr Cruncher, going on again, and lifting off his hat to give his spikes free play, 'he's a tradesman.'

'What's his goods, Father?' asked the brisk Young Jerry.

'His goods,' said Mr Cruncher, after turning it over in his mind, 'is a branch of scientific goods.'

'Persons' bodies, ain't it, Father?' asked the lively boy.

'I believe it is something of that sort,' said Mr Cruncher.

'Oh, Father, I should so like to be a resurrection-man when I'm quite growed up!'

Mr Cruncher was soothed, but shook his head in a dubious and moral way. 'It depends upon how you dewelop your talents. Be careful to dewelop your talents, and never to say no more than you can help to nobody, and there's no telling at the present time what you may not come to be fit for.' As Young Jerry, thus encouraged, went on a few yards in advance, to plant the stool in the shadow of the Bar, Mr Cruncher added to himself: 'Jerry, you honest tradesman, there's hopes wot that boy will yet be a blessing to you, and a recompense to you for his mother!'

The script has been started for you.

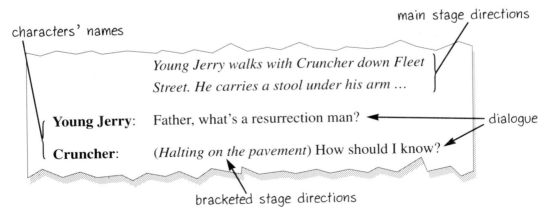

characters' names

main stage directions

Young Jerry walks with Cruncher down Fleet Street. He carries a stool under his arm …

Young Jerry: Father, what's a resurrection man? ← dialogue

Cruncher: (*Halting on the pavement*) How should I know?

bracketed stage directions

Write   Carry on with the adaptation.

Appendix

Mime Techniques

In the Prologue, Scene 1, the following stage direction appears: *Cruncher glides backwards to give the impression that the coach is in motion.* The idea here is that things move relative to each other. If you look out of the window of a train as it starts off, it can appear that the station is moving and the train is still. Similarly, if Cruncher appears to be standing still while he is moving backwards, the coach and passengers will appear to be moving forwards though they are really stationary.

This is a mime technique and essentially it is very like Michael Jackson's 'moonwalking' – although not quite as flamboyant. The illusion of stillness is given by keeping your upper body as if you were standing still while your legs carry you backwards apparently without your noticing, as if they belong to someone else.

In the Prologue, Scene 2, you will find the following stage direction: *Defarge, leading, then Lorry, then Lucie begin to ascend a long stair...* This also calls for another mime technique. The trick is to step on the balls of your feet, so that your body rises, then lower your foot so that it is flat to the floor and your body sinks. At the same time, with one hand, you 'hold' an imaginary bannister rail, and your hand moves backwards and downwards as you step. The step can be done on the spot or as you are moving. The aim is to give the audience the impression that you are climbing the stairs.

It always helps if you can arrange for a trained mime artist to demonstrate these techniques. (See also Act 1, Scene 2: *Gabelle, the roadmender and the peasants glide backwards to give the impression that the carriage is moving.*)

Lighting

Look at the following stage direction in the Prologue, Scene 2: *A bright beam of light strikes Doctor Manette...* Here, we are suggesting that you reinforce Defarge's mime of opening the shutters with a lighting change. By shining a window gobo on this scene, you can create the impression of daylight flooding into Doctor Manette's cell.

The Guillotine

The guillotine can be represented by a shadow-play model. First you will need a small working model of a guillotine (this can be two dimensional). Then you need to project its image on a back wall (this can be flat or cyclorama) using a fresnel type lantern. A blue gel in the lantern will give the impression of sky in the background (the intensity of the colour filter can be changed to represent different times of day, and to reinforce this you might use cloud gobos or moving effects). See diagram below.

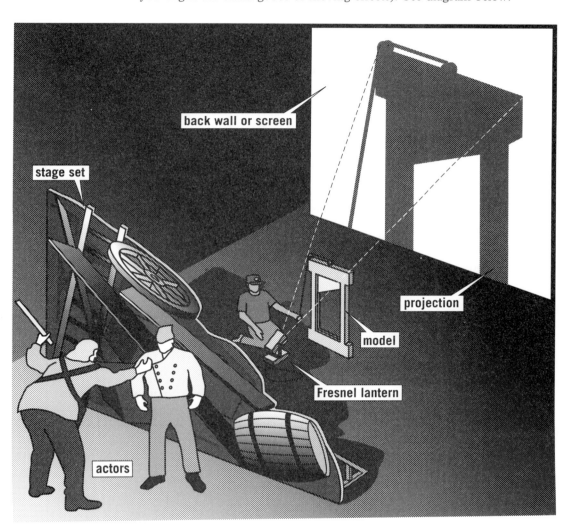

Plays in this series include:

Across the Barricades   ISBN 0 19 831272 5
  Joan Lingard   adapted by David Ian Neville

The Bonny Pit Laddie   ISBN 0 19 831278 4
  Frederick Grice   adapted by David Spraggon Williams
                       with Frank Green

The Burston School Strike   ISBN 0 19 831274 1
  Roy Nevitt

The Demon Headmaster   ISBN 0 19 831270 9
  Gillian Cross   adapted by Adrian Flynn

Frankenstein   ISBN 0 19 831267 9
  Mary Shelley   adapted by Philip Pullman

Hot Cakes   ISBN 0 19 831273 3
  Adrian Flynn

Johnny and the Dead   ISBN 0 19 831294 6
  Terry Pratchett   adapted by Stephen Briggs

Paper Tigers   ISBN 0 19 831268 7
  Steve Barlow and Steve Skidmore

A Question of Courage   ISBN 0 19 831271 7
  Marjorie Darke   adapted by Bill Lucas and Brian Keaney

The Teen Commandments   ISBN 0 19 831275 X
  Kelvin Reynolds

Tigers on the Prowl   ISBN 0 19 831277 6
  Steve Barlow and Steve Skidmore

The Turbulent Term of Tyke Tiler   ISBN 0 19 831269 5
  adapted from her own novel by Gene Kemp